In memory of Christine Mackay (1942-2005)

Things fall apart...

Museum conservation in practice

Edited by Caroline Buttler and Mary Davis

National Museum Wales Books

Things fall apart; the centre cannot hold
W. B. Yeats, *The Second Coming* (1921)

First published in 2006 by National Museum Wales Books,
Cathays Park, Cardiff, CF10 3NP, Wales.

ISBN 0 7200 0559 0

Editing and production: Mari Gordon
Design: Peter Gill & Associates

Acknowledgements

There are several key people without whom this book would never have happened. Richard Brewer offered encouragement and support from the outset and enabled the idea to become a reality. Bob Child was similarly encouraging and provided help with many of the texts when we started to flag. Edward Besly and Simon Buttler read all the chapters and offered continuous advice; Edward, with his experience, gave much constructive guidance. Mari Gordon provided practical and editorial assistance. Most of all we need to thank those who wrote the chapters and made the book happen.

Many of these chapters could only have been written and researched with the help of colleagues: some carried out the actual conservation work described, others offered advice, undertook analyses, read texts and provided illustrations. Their contributions have been essential and the editors and authors of each chapter would like to thank the following:
Paola Bevilacqua, Kathy Bird, Daniel Bone, Kenneth Brassil, Richard Brewer, Alberto Campagnolo, Jackie Chadwick, Mike Corfield, Tom Cotterell, Peter Crew, Adam Gwilt, Tony Daly, John Davies, Ruth Davis, Sandrine Decoux, Yaron Ever-Hadani, Susan Fox, Paul Giudici, Hero Granger Taylor, Tony Hadland, Jane Henderson, Ray Howell, Elan Jones, Mike Lambert, Bethan Lewis, David Maynard, Robert Pearce, Toby Petersen, Frances Pritchard, Heather Prosser, Robert Protheroe-Jones, Jenny Radcliffe, Mark Redknap, Julie Reynolds, Alison Stooshnov, Clare Stoughton-Harris, Alan Sutton, Julie Taylor, Kevin Thomas, Ceri Thompson, Peter Walker, Jim Wild, Louise Window, Katharina Wollny, Mark Worthington.

The authors would also like to thank the following organizations:
The School of History and Archaeology, Cardiff University; Countryside Council for Wales; Dow Corning Corporation; The Royal Commission on the Ancient & Historic Monuments of Wales; The School of Technology, University of Glamorgan; The Tree-Ring Dating Laboratory, Nottingham University.

Contents

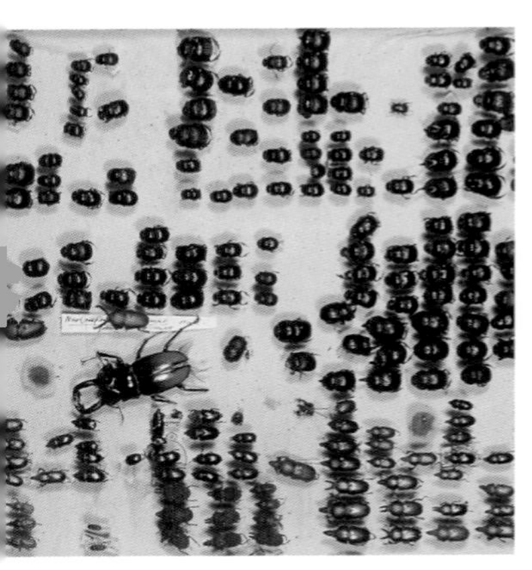

Re-conservation and restoration

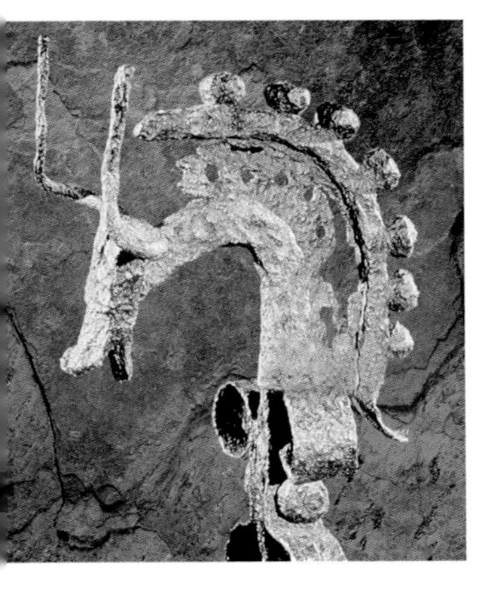

Moulding, casting and replication

Glossary

Contributors

Caroline Buttler, Geological Conservator, Department of Geology, National Museum of Wales.

Julian Carter, Zoological Conservator, Department of Biodiversity & Systematic Biology, National Museum of Wales.

Robert Child, Head of Conservation, National Museum of Wales.

Emyr Davies, Furniture Conservator, Department of Social & Cultural History, National Museum of Wales.

Mary Davis, Archaeological Conservator, Department of Archaeology & Numismatics, National Museum of Wales.

Walter Gneisinger, Objects Conservator, Department of Industry, National Museum of Wales.

Penny Hill, Archaeological Conservator, Department of Archaeology & Numismatics, National Museum of Wales.

Stephen Howe, Head of Programmes and Presentation, National Museum of Wales.

Sioned Wyn Hughes, Curator of Historic Buildings and Commerce, Department of Social & Cultural History, National Museum of Wales.

Kate Hunter, The Newport Ship Project Leader, Newport Museum & Art Gallery. Formerly Archaeological Conservator, Department of Archaeology & Numismatics, National Museum of Wales.

Mark Lewis, Curatorial Officer, National Roman Legion Museum, National Museum of Wales; Demonstrator in Conservation at Cardiff University.

Kate Lowry, Paintings Conservator, Department of Art, National Museum of Wales.

Christine Mackay, Paper Conservator. Formerly Department of Art, National Museum of Wales.

Chris Meechan, Scientific Illustrator, Department of Biodiversity & Systematic Biology, National Museum of Wales.

Louise Mumford, Archaeological Conservator, Department of Archaeology & Numismatics, National Museum of Wales.

Gerallt Nash, Head of Historic Buildings & Commerce, Department of Social & Cultural History, National Museum of Wales.

Chris Perry, Technician, Department of Industry, National Museum of Wales.

David Petersen, Artist-blacksmith. Formerly Exhibiting Craftsman, St Fagans National History Museum, National Museum of Wales.

Victoria Purewal, Botanical Conservator,
Department of Biodiversity & Systematic Biology,
National Museum of Wales.

Sue Renault, Social History Conservator,
Department of Social & Cultural History,
National Museum of Wales.

Annette Townsend, Conservator/Model Maker,
Department of Biodiversity & Systematic
Biology, National Museum of Wales.

Rachel Turnbull, Paintings Conservator,
Department of Art, National Museum of Wales.

Felicity Woor, Treasure Registrar, The British Museum.
Formerly Conservation Intern, Department of
Archaeology & Numismatics, National Museum
of Wales.

Introduction

For as long as people have appreciated art for art's sake, there has been a tradition of care, maintenance, repair and restoration. However, it is only in the last 150 years or so that preserving works of art, archaeology and natural history has become a science, and only in the last fifty years has conservation become a recognized subject in its own right.

Conservation – as it is now known – embraces three aspects: examination, preservation and restoration. Examination determines the nature of the object, its materials and methods of construction, and its deterioration. Preservation attempts to slow down or stop the agents of deterioration in order to preserve the innate originality of the object. Restoration is the most subjective aspect, in that it attempts to return an object to a former state. The French philosopher Étienne Gilson (1884-1978) stated 'there are two ways for a painting to perish. One is for it to be restored; the other is for it not to be'. Herein lies the dilemma for all those engaged in conservation. Examination and preservation – now usually referred to as 'passive conservation' – are normally non-controversial and follow well-established procedures. Restoration, being subjective, changes with time, fashion and opinion. The controversies still raging over the restoration of the Sistine Chapel ceiling and the Elgin Marbles only highlight the differences in opinions held by different factions. The controversy between 'preservation' and restoration has been described as the difference between walking over a pile of rubble and walking under an arch.

Museums acquire their collections in many ways. A suite of paintings may be bequeathed by a collector, or items may be donated when they are of no further use or interest to the owner. A museum will often acquire specific items such as research collections from scientists by purchase, loan or fieldwork as well as through active collecting policies. By all these means, large quantities of 'new' material is acquired, not all of it in good condition and all of it in need of preservation.

The National Museum of Wales is relatively unusual for a national museum in that it collects, curates and conserves most categories of natural sciences, history and the arts. Although its collections are international, there is obviously a strong focus on the cultural and natural history of Wales.

The acquisition of so many different collections from such a variety of sources obviously stems from a number of philosophies. Items will be collected for immediate exhibition, others for examination and research and others to be preserved from permanent loss, perhaps because they have a social ephemeral nature. A quart milk bottle from a now defunct local dairy is an example of this.

Curators responsible for the diversity of their collections often have fewer ethical dilemmas than their conservation colleagues: they will know exactly why they have collected a particular material. Conservators, however, are often faced with a number of intellectual and pragmatic dilemmas. The variety of possible remedial treatments available are legion but are increasingly subservient to ethical considerations. Readers of the seminal *The Conservation of Antiquities and Works of Art* (Plenderleith 1956) today will be struck by the fact that it is almost a recipe book of treatments that can be applied in all circumstances. For instance, if an object is corroded, the book explains how to remove the corrosion, but says little about whether or not we *should* remove the corrosion.

However, conservation ethics, like all cultural attitudes, change and move on. The ground-breaking advances made by Plenderleith have now been superseded by major advances in the sciences. Non-invasive analytical techniques and imaging processes allow us to understand and visualise objects without damaging or affecting them deleteriously. Destructive sampling is now rarely used and ethical stances on restorations have changed. Even books on conservation practice published relatively recently such as *The Art of the Conservator* (Oddy 1992) illustrate conservation and restoration practices carried out in the 1970s and 80s that might not now be considered ethical.

Increasingly, we can find out more from our subjects with less and less active intervention and damage. Passive or preventative conservation not only preserves the morphology of an object, but also keeps intact the wealth of scientific information within it. Advances in analytical techniques and products allow us to tap that information in greater depth and enhance our knowledge of many more aspects of the object.

Conservation today is a fast-moving, developing science and art. As it develops, so the ethical values change. There are no conservation axioms or recipes that are universally applicable: each object has to be considered for its own needs, to enhance aspects of its interpretation.

This volume illustrates the current status quo of a major Western national museum with strong collecting, curating, conserving, researching and exhibiting policies. It demonstrates how objectives have changed in the last fifty years – and continue to change.

It takes a diverse selection of conservation projects from a number of disciplines, and examines the different approaches taken to present the information the objects present to the viewer or researcher. It looks at traditional and new methods of preservation and how the general trend of preventative conservation exists today. The book is intended to act as a benchmark for today's analytical and ethical standards. How those standards will last, and how they might change, remains to be seen.

Robert Child

ODDY, A. 1992. *The Art of the Conservator.* British Museum Press, London.

PLENDERLEITH, H. J. 1956. *The Conservation of Antiquities and Works of Art.* Oxford University Press, London.

Preventative conservation

Make yourself at home
Looking after an open-air museum

Breaking the code
Conserving DNA – new demands on natural science collections

Conserving a coal mine
Keeping our industrial heritage working

Non calor sed umor est qui nobis incommodat. (It ain't the heat it's the humidity that bothers us.)

Conservation is the means by which we try to preserve the life of some pertinent aspect of an object. Preventative conservation concentrates on the environment around the object, and attempts to provide the optimum conditions for the object to have a long and uneventful life. Unfortunately, the conditions for preservation are often diametrically opposed to those required by the public and researchers to appreciate and enjoy the object. High light levels aid vision, but increase fading; the warmer the temperature the happier the museum visitor is, and the quicker the materials deteriorate. Open access allows pollution, dust, insects, bad handling and theft, but gives the viewing public a better appreciation of the exhibitions and displays.

In 1850, Dr Gustave Frederick Waagen, Director of the Royal Gallery in Berlin, when reporting to the Parliamentary Select Committee on the National Gallery stated that:
The greatest enemy to pictures is damp: and to avoid this we have a system of maintaining a medium temperature, not too cold and not too warm. In the winter ... all the rooms are heated with warm air: but to avoid the great dryness of that air in every place a vessel with water is placed in each room, and the air is moistened by the water ... and that is not

only useful for the pictures, but it is also useful for the public; because otherwise the air would be too dry, and not wholesome.

Over 150 years later, conservators and curators are still struggling with these basic issues of environmental control and the dilemmas associated with both displaying and preserving objects in their care.

Preventative conservation is not an exact science, but tries to address the dichotomy between the two forces faced by museums: conservation and interpretation. The value of an object may not just lie in its appearance or morphology, but can be in its internal structure, its use or other such aspects, as this section demonstrates. Preventative conservation highlights these positive aspects and aims to maintain them for the longest appropriate time by the best appropriate methods.

Make yourself at home
Looking after an open-air museum

St Fagans National History Museum in Cardiff is the longest established open-air museum in the UK. The Earl of Plymouth donated St Fagans Castle, a late sixteenth-century manor house, and its surrounding gardens to the National Museum of Wales in 1946, and it opened to its first visitors in July 1948 as the Welsh Folk Museum, with an entry fee of a shilling (5p). Since then, buildings have been collected from all over Wales and re-erected on the site, each furnished to a particular period with items from the national collections. Over the past fifty years it has inspired millions of visitors with an appreciation of Welsh history and traditions.

The ethos of the Museum has been to make the visitor feel that the interiors they are seeing are as believable as possible, and physical access has been a priority. Very few restrictions have been placed on the visitor, and the friendly welcome they traditionally receive is a strong feature of the Museum's attraction. However, the cracks, quite

Below left: St Fagans Castle

literally, began to show as years of handling and display in uncontrolled environments began to take their toll on the individual objects.

Agents of decay

Even in the most perfect museum environments, objects can still decay. In the majority of cases a combination of factors causes the damage. Probably the easiest way to understand the inter-relationships between these factors is to consider a single object. For example, a simply constructed wooden table. Four planks of pine form the top, with two nails at each end of the planks to hold them to the frame below. The four legs are bolted onto the frame. The top of the table, the outer surfaces of the frame and all surfaces of the legs are finished with a polyurethane varnish. To begin with, the heat and ultraviolet light from any sunlight falling on the tabletop cause the varnish to yellow as it becomes chemically degraded. If subjected to constant fluctuations of temperature and relative humidity, the planks of the tabletop begin to split and warp. The warping results because the upper surfaces of the planks are sealed by the varnish and are therefore no longer affected by changes in the moisture content of the air, whilst the lower surfaces can still expand and contract. Where the nails are restricting the freedom of the planks to undergo expansion and contraction, cracks will appear. The high relative humidity that causes the wood to swell will also cause the nails and bolts to corrode. This corrosion will be quickened by the natural acidity of the wood. As the metal corrodes, metal oxides begin to form on the outer surfaces of the nails, leaching into the surrounding wood and causing staining of the wood and slow loss of the nail.

As well as physical and chemical decay, the table is also susceptible to biological decay. High relative humidity can result in mould growth, and the pine is also susceptible to attack by woodworm. The larvae of this beetle munch away inside the wood, forming innumerable empty corridors before pupating just below the surface and then emerging through the tell-tale holes. Once it has undergone a woodworm attack the wood becomes more susceptible to moisture changes and, depending on the extent and the location of the damage, can become structurally unstable. If the table stands on an uneven floor for a long period of time, settling occurs whereby the table shapes itself to compensate for some of the legs being on lower ground than the others. If the table were then to be moved to an even surface, it would wobble. All this damage can easily occur if the table is displayed in an uncontrolled environment.

The table is an example of a composite object, constructed from more than one material. The major concern with all composite objects is the effect their materials of construction will have on one another. Treating these objects usually means having to compromise. The best example of this is in choosing the optimum relative humidity at which to display the object. For a wooden-handled knife, the wood, being organic, is best kept at approximately 55 to 60 per cent relative humidity, whilst to prevent the blade from corroding the knife would need as low a relative humidity as possible, preferably below 20 per cent. Without physically separating the handle from the blade, which is an option but would make interpretation difficult, the only solution is to choose a relative humidity in the middle.

Perhaps the most awkward composite objects we deal with at St Fagans are the buildings themselves. They are part of the national collections,

A Welsh dresser on display at St Fagans

and they are in constant use. In 2001, free entry was introduced to all National Museum of Wales sites and since then the number of visitors to St Fagans has doubled to nearly 700,000 a year. The daily wear and tear by the visitors on buildings originally intended for a handful of occupants now exacts a heavy toll on their fabric. Even on the stone floors it is possible to see the visitor tracks where the floor has eroded; this is even more visible in the buildings with traditional recipe mud floors. In the parlour of a seventeenth-century farm house, the central table and chairs now sit on an island of solid floor formed as the surrounding area has been literally walked away. However, year-round opening means that it is impossible to undertake the required maintenance outside of opening hours. Instead, the buildings have to be closed on a rota basis to cause least impact on visitor enjoyment.

Display of the collections

A common feature of all the display environments at the Museum of Welsh Life, with the exception of the galleries in the main building, is the juxtaposition of the objects. The dressers have plates on them, the beds are dressed and the shelves and sideboards are laden with knick-knacks. In choosing a dresser for display, its condition needs to be considered: will it bear the weight of the items on it? Could the items chosen to sit on the dresser scratch it? How can we minimise the risks? This type of analysis of individual objects is preventative conservation at a micro level.

The types of display can be loosely divided into three. The first of these is the more conventional museum gallery, with objects displayed in cases or in roped areas. Here, the objects are protected from handling and are displayed in a controllable climate. Security is also less problematic and the objects tend to be the best examples, often of higher monetary value and historical status. The same can be said of the second display type, the interior of St Fagans Castle. This is similar to the way the National Trust displays the contents of country houses, with the majority of objects of higher quality mainly on view behind barrier ropes.

The third type of display is the re-erected buildings themselves, located over much of the site. These displays have one major common feature: the public – up close and personal. The objects are reachable and all are fair game for handling. In fact, observations on site have shown that the more recognizable objects are to the visitor, the more likely they are to handle them.

Before any building is opened to the public, careful consideration is given to an object's proximity to the visitor route, weighed against its fragility. Certain types of material are particularly

A farmhouse heated by an open fire, and with no electricity

vulnerable: the textiles and many of the paper-based exhibits in the cottages are not accessioned, and are regarded as relatively expendable. These are items used as 'set dressing', in the certain knowledge that they will be worn away by handling and/or decay in the harsh environment of the historic interiors. The open fires that make the buildings so inviting and aid interpretation are actually depositing acidic soot on the contents, corroding the metals and dirtying everything. Combine this with the greasy, acidic deposits left after handling and the high moisture contents in the buildings and you have a recipe for decay.

The environments within these buildings can be loosely separated into two further subdivisions: those with electricity and those without. In buildings with no electricity, the fire is our only means of environmental control. Unfortunately, because the fire can only safely be alight during visitor hours when it can be attended, the relative humidity can vary by as much as 30 per cent. For a bulky piece of furniture this is not too serious because it takes a couple of days for the change to register, but for smaller and less dense organic objects these fluctuations can cause serious damage. This is particularly true of objects that are restricted by

Kennixton farmhouse dates from 1610 and comes from the Gower in south-west Wales. It was re-erected at St Fagans in 1955. The red colour of the walls was thought to protect the house against evil spirits.

their construction: the swelling and contraction of an organic material around a fixed point creates internal stresses that often result in cracks or tears. Of course this is not immediately noticeable to the visitor since the lighting in these buildings is low. Without electricity, illumination is provided by authentic period systems such as candles and oil lamps, or by the harsher modern gas camping lanterns, all of which have their own particular limitations.
The cleaning staff have the unenviable task, using brushes and lint-free dusters, of trying to rid these buildings of the soot produced by fires and lighting methods and the dust emanating from the hundreds of visitors per day. Despite heroic efforts this can sometimes be little more than a disturbance rather than a removal.

Where a building has electricity available it is possible to alleviate the effects of dampness by using low background heat and installing dehumidifiers. The first experiments in this area were carried out using night storage heaters hidden beneath the counters in two reconstructed shops. Their success was limited because of the accessibility of the controls. On a cold day, there was always the temptation for staff to adjust the boost control so that on subsequent days the temperature within the building would soar. The most effective approach to date has been the introduction of underfloor heating. When the 1940s prefab house was recently erected this discreet form of heating was installed under the floorboards. It now runs night and day through the cold months at a constant 10°C, acting as background heating and ironing out the temperature fluctuations between night and day. This allows a greater range of objects to be displayed.

© Photolibrary Wales

The Preventative Conservation Policy

The advent of free entry to the Museum has made all members of staff re-evaluate why things are done and how. It has become obvious that if we are to present the site to its best advantage, not just to today's visitors but also to future visitors, then we cannot simply continue as we are; we have to make changes. Through collaboration and consultation we have written a preventative conservation policy specifically for St Fagans. The stated intention is to allow access to the collection whilst substantially reducing the risk of damaging the accessioned objects.

For the policy to work it is necessary to deliver relevant and continued training. The next step therefore is to devise and implement training schemes for any member of staff handling the collection. Controlling handling will to a degree limit physical damage to the collection but it cannot work in isolation. Despite the best will in the world, accidental damage is inevitable in overcrowded buildings. As mentioned earlier, the buildings on site are now subjected to a use that is above and beyond that for which any of them were designed. Of necessity, agreed visitor limits exist for all display areas. Until recently the implementation of this preventative measure has been the sole responsibility of the staff on duty in the building. We have now begun to experiment with the use of signs and all areas are currently under assessment with regard to the use of channelling systems. Such measures lift the weight of responsibility from the individual member of staff, providing them with a supervisory role and making it clear to the public that their authority comes from the institution. Signs also allow us to explain why numbers have to be limited, so that the visitor can understand the reasons for the policy.

Implementation of the visitor limits has another advantage. Not only is accidental damage to the collection reduced, whether this is through bumping against furniture or knocking and smashing ceramics, but it also makes security easier. By reducing the numbers inside the building at any one time, it is now possible for staff to watch the collection and thus fulfil their security role.

With such a vast array of objects on open display, constructed from a wide variety of materials, keeping the collection clean is no easy task. Specialist knowledge of the cleaning methods to be employed in individual buildings is essential to avoid unintentional damage. During the process of writing the policy it was recognized that the damage caused by inappropriate cleaning far outweighs any that dust sitting on an object will do whilst waiting for a trained cleaner to become available. It has shifted the balance from the apparent all-consuming need to clean for the sake of it towards cleaning in a controlled and informed way.

It has long been recognized that frequent polishing of plated metals causes the irreversible loss of the plating, so that the silver-plated trophy turns to brass; but the same idea holds true for many materials within the collection. Stone floor erosion is in part attributable to the frequent mopping that has occurred over many years, with over-wetting assisting the breakdown of the surface. Discontinuing inappropriate cleaning methods and zoning the displays into areas that need daily, weekly or monthly cleaning makes the whole process more manageable. It also opens up the possibility of giving the cleaning staff ownership of the buildings they are trained to clean, and using them for tasks such as insect monitoring to aid the 'housekeeping' conservators in their constant battle to prevent infestation. In order to cement this bond between the cleaners and the housekeeping conservators, we are piloting an induction training scheme whereby any new cleaner will spend their first week working alongside one of our housekeepers. During this week, the housekeeper can impart the conservation aims within the individual buildings, the role of good preventative conservation and the importance of the cleaner in the process.

The housekeeping conservators have a pivotal role in safeguarding the collection. It is essential that they are informed of all activities, events and maintenance requirements at the planning stage so that they can ensure that appropriate safeguards are in place and all the relevant staff are consulted. This has to include every member of staff, because no matter what job we do, whether curator, cleaner, typist or electrician, the collection is what makes us a museum. On the basest level, safeguarding the collection is, in effect, protecting our jobs: on the noblest level, safeguarding the collection is protecting the cultural heritage of Wales.

Fundamental to the protection of the collection is the provision of an appropriate display environment. Despite being based on an open-air site, the conservation staff constantly strive to achieve the best standards set out by the Museums, Libraries and Archives Council. We are driven by the belief that we must continuously review and adapt the methods of environmental control at our disposal. Discussions surrounding the formation of the conservation policy made everyone aware of how vital electricity is to the care and protection of the collection. As a result, agreement has been reached that consideration will be given to finding the most beneficial heating system for all new buildings, and the installation of electricity is an absolute necessity. More than this, there is now an undertaking to install electricity in all the existing buildings on the site as soon as practicable, given the constraints of resources available, and also to draw up a plan for installing heating systems.

One of the hardest concepts to get across to both staff and the public is that once an object becomes part of the collection there has to be a separation of form from function. It is all too easy to forget this when there is not a clear visual separation of objects for public or staff use from objects in the collection. For example, accessioned furniture is widely used for storing the newspapers used to light the fires. Hinges are being worn by daily use, the weight of the newspapers is causing structural stress, and this is magnified as the papers absorb moisture from the atmosphere, creating a damp microclimate inside the cupboard and encouraging mould growth. Clearly a change of practice is required. For some buildings, storage of such materials could be accommodated in an area out of public view. Alternatively, the answer may be a return to authentic fire-lighting methods, appropriate to the period of the house. Whatever the solution in the individual buildings, the result will be that the public will no longer see staff opening pieces of furniture and they will therefore no longer feel encouraged to follow suit. This is one example of many mixed messages we currently send out to the public and which, through the policy, we hope to address.

The policy in practice

St Fagans has always sought to display its buildings as realistically as possible. Over time the interiors have slowly lost this realism as objects fell apart, were withdrawn – or simply stolen. Sparse interiors have slowly become the trend because they have proved to be more sustainable. The visitor goes away with the sense that people from earlier periods lived with next to no possessions, and so we are creating a false impression.

In the bedroom of Kennixton farmhouse, dating to the seventeenth century, despite the occupants having been relatively prosperous, there are no small personal items on display (see p.15). How did they amuse their children, brush their hair or even light their rooms? With such items being too rare, valuable, fragile or portable, they could not be risked on open display in a building with five rooms and only one member of staff present for security. The result is a sterile room relieved only by the replica textiles adorning the bed.

Compare this to the bedroom in the prefab. Here the room is adorned with personal items. This is not just possible because items from the 1940s are more easily available, but mainly because they have the protection of being in a roped off area. In this sense, it can be argued that slightly restricted physical access to the collection in the form of a barrier actually makes a much larger proportion of the collection visually accessible. We do not intend to

The bedroom of the Museum's 1940s prefab

use the preventative conservation policy as a tool to separate the visitor from the collection, but rather to use it to enhance their experience. In terms of implementing the policy, we are only just beginning but, if we get it right, the visitor will be impressed by the care all our staff lavish on the collection and they will take away a sense of how highly we value the objects, not simply for themselves, but for the history and culture they represent.

Sue Renault

SANDWITH, H. & STAINTON, S. 2005. *The National Trust Manual of Housekeeping*. Viking, London.

The upstairs bedroom in Kennixton farmhouse

Breaking the code
Conserving DNA – new demands on natural science collections

Over three million biological specimens are housed at the National Museum of Wales, including thousands of different species of plants, animals and fungi. Museums hold some of the most important collections of natural science material in the UK, with some institutions holding specimens collected over 300 years ago. The collections were originally put together as 'curiosities', but were subsequently developed by dedicated scientific expeditions. These specimens have been used to form the basis of our ideas on issues such as evolution, ecology and taxonomy and they continue to play an important role in research and education. As the pressure on our natural environment and its flora and fauna increases, these collections are becoming an ever more important resource for both traditional morphological studies and modern genetic studies. Museum collections are particularly useful in that, as well as containing many different species, they also span time and geography. They become of even greater value when many of the species collected are now either extinct or so highly endangered that further collection is not possible, or not viable due to financial or political reasons. The result is that many of these specimens form an irreplaceable record that is vital in developing our understanding of various biological processes, especially in key issues such as biodiversity and climate change.

Preserving biological material can be very difficult. Upon death, physiological and cellular control processes are lost and autolytic decay sets in. This decay causes the destruction of cells by enzymes produced by the organism itself and, if unchecked, this results in rapid degradation. Museum fixation and preservation treatments are aimed at halting the processes of autolytic decay, allowing the long-term preservation of biological material. This can involve the specimens being passed through a series of treatments before reaching the final method of preservation.

The preservation of natural science material was initially only possible for dry inert materials. It was not until the development of fluid preservation that it became possible to preserve moist, soft biological material. The practice of fluid preservation dates back to 1644 when Croone presented to the Royal Society two whole puppies preserved in the 'spirit of wine' (ethyl alcohol). Later, towards the end of the nineteenth century, the properties of formaldehyde were discovered. Formaldehyde is used to fix biological tissue chemically in order to stop it degrading, and its use has become widespread in museums. These practices have changed very little over the last century, and alcohol and formaldehyde solutions are still amongst the most important techniques available for the preservation of biological tissue. The result is that many of the methods used in museums are based on what appears to have worked, rather than hard scientific evaluation.

Recent years have seen the development of new demands on museum biological collections. There has been a rapid development and improvement in the technology and techniques used in microbiological research. Of particular note is the development of the Polymerase Chain Reaction (PCR), which has enabled researchers to replicate and amplify very small amounts of DNA for subsequent analysis. DNA, or deoxyribonucleic acid, is a long double-helix molecule that carries the genetic coding information for a species, and is contained in every cell of an organism. The result is that very small quantities of DNA can now be extracted from museum specimens, and then replicated until there is sufficient DNA for a

A specimen of the extinct Tasmanian wolf (*Thylacius cynocephalus*); the last known animal died in captivity in 1936

researcher to work with. The DNA is used in many areas of study, such as evolution, species identification and ecology. This new accessibility to the genetic information of species, and the growing crisis in the world's biodiversity, means that museum collections are now being increasingly used as a resource for microbiological studies. Examples of such studies include:

- Work on the extinct Tasmanian wolf to see how it related to existing marsupials.
- Identification of difficult groups of organisms such as mosquitoes, allowing the accurate identification of malaria-carrying species.
- The identification and the distribution of Lyme's disease by examining the blood in preserved ticks for the DNA of the bacteria responsible for it. The disease is characterised in humans by neuralgic, cardiac and rheumatic conditions and can be fatal.

The result is that there is now a need for those caring for biological collections to have a better understanding of how the methods used to conserve the specimens affect the integrity of the DNA held within them. By improving this understanding it should be possible to improve specimen preservation for both morphological and molecular study as cost effectively as possible.

Many factors will affect the condition of the DNA in a specimen. These include the preservation history and the age of the material. Autolytic decay causes the rapid degradation of DNA molecules from the effects of enzymes and reactive molecules in the tissues. Preservation treatments aim to halt the decay processes, but can themselves have an effect on the condition of the DNA. The DNA can also be affected by factors such as hydrolysis, oxidation, radiation and temperature. All these processes can

A deep sea spider (Pygnogonida) preserved in formaldehyde

cause structural changes to the DNA molecules including:

- Denaturation, where the duplex DNA molecule becomes separated into single stranded DNA which is more open to chemical attack.
- Cross-linking reactions which bond the duplex DNA to each other or other molecules such as proteins, making the DNA less accessible.
- Strand breakages or nicks in the sugar phosphate backbone of the DNA molecules causing fragmentation.
- Chemical modification of nucleotides which carry the genetic coding, through addition, removal, or replacement of chemical groups. This can cause changes in the nucleotide sequence or alter the way the DNA reacts chemically.

The best method we currently have for the storage of specimens for molecular analysis is freezing, known as cryo-preservation. This can be done in liquid nitrogen, or by the use of -80°C freezers. However, cryo-preserved collections require constant monitoring and are expensive to maintain. For these reasons they are not a practical consideration for many natural history museums. In addition cryo-preservation will not preserve the morphology of a specimen, at least not in a way that makes the specimen accessible. So how do other methods of fixation and preservation used with natural science collections affect the condition of the DNA?

Some of the first published DNA studies using museum specimens looked at extinct or rare animals. The material used for these studies was dried muscle, skin, feather or bone and tended to provide DNA that was around 200-300 base pairs long. Whilst this DNA was essentially degraded, it proved usable for cloning, hybridisation and PCR. During this period, workers were also beginning to look at using the DNA stored in archival histopathological material fixed in formaldehyde, or some other chemical fixative, and then embedded in paraffin. The successful extraction of DNA surviving in such material demonstrated that biological tissue that had been exposed to a whole range of chemical treatments could still have a viable use in DNA studies. This view has been further reinforced from studies with ancient DNA obtained from archaeological and subfossil remains.

The establishment of usable DNA in museum

Dried entomological specimens

specimens that were originally collected for their gross morphological features has led to the consideration of a wide range of museum preserved specimens for subsequent molecular work, including fluid-preserved material. As the use of preserved material in DNA studies increased, consideration began to be given to the effects of museum preservation treatments on the condition of the DNA and the reliability of any analysis carried out, such as the reading of DNA sequences. Some of the resulting studies showed that the DNA that could be extracted from formaldehyde fixed material tended to be of low molecular weight, whereas ethanol fixed and preserved material potentially yielded high molecular weight DNA. It is thus considered that fixatives such as formaldehyde either badly degrade the DNA or alter it chemically, making extraction and analysis of the DNA difficult. The preservative action of ethanol on DNA is thought to be related to its dehydrating and 'pseudo-fixative' effect on proteins, in which water is removed and proteins are preserved by structural, rather than chemical, changes. Ethanol however does not preserve the external morphology, histology and internal anatomy as well as formaldehyde does.

Drying is also a widely used method of preservation in museums. Many different groups of organisms can be preserved in a dry form, and many specimens are subsequently dried following fluid preservation. Drying is a particularly useful method with many groups of insects. How the specimen is dried can affect the integrity of the DNA, for example entomologists use ethyl acetate to kill and prepare specimens for dry pinning, and this has been found to preserve DNA very poorly. Specialised drying techniques such as Critical Point Drying, and certain chemical drying methods potentially give both good morphological and good DNA preservation.

We have been further assessing many of the preservation processes listed in the table opposite. The results obtained from this research have reaffirmed many of the findings of previous studies considering the problems of molecular preservation. However some additional observations have been noted, especially with the use of ethanol-based solutions. One of the most important methods of preservation we use involves the use of Industrial Methylated Spirits (IMS). The use of methyl alcohol

A summary of the effects of various preservation protocols on invertebrate specimens (after Thomas 1994, Reiss et al. 1996, Dillon et al. 1996, Quicke et al. 1999)

Mode of fixation	Subsequent preservation	External morphology	Histology	Internal anatomy	DNA
Cryo preservation	Freezer at −70°C or below.	Can be Good	Poor	Fair to Good	Good
Absolute ethanol	Absolute ethanol	Poor to Good	Poor to Fair	Poor to Fair	Good
70-80% IMS	70-80% IMS	Fair to Good	Fair to Good	Fair to Good	Fair to Good
70-80% IMS	CPD or chemical drying	Good	Poor	Good	Fair to Good
70-80% IMS	Air drying	Good for certain groups.	Poor	Variable	Fair
4% Formaldehyde	70-80% IMS	Fair to Good	Fair	Fair	Poor to Fair
4% Formaldehyde	4% Formaldehyde	Good	Fair to Good	Good	Poor
Ethyl acetate	Air dried	Fair to Good	?	Variable	Very Poor
Formaldehyde-based histological	Same	Fair to Good	Good	Good	Very Poor to Poor
Mercury based histological	Same	Fair to Good	Good	Good	None or Very Poor

in IMS, to make it unfit for consumption, allows the alcohol duty costs to be dropped, making it considerably cheaper to purchase than absolute ethanol. A growing concern is whether the use of IMS as a preserving fluid is as good as ethanol preservation for the condition of whole genomic DNA. Recent work suggests that IMS preservation does have an effect on the condition of the DNA within a specimen. While high molecular weight DNA can be extracted, analysis suggests that the IMS preservation process has weakened the DNA, although it remains usable in molecular analyses. Using IMS also causes similar morphological preservation problems to absolute ethanol. These problems can be reduced by diluting the IMS solutions to 80 per cent IMS, and by using additives such as propylene glycol. However the use of 80 per cent IMS solutions causes an immediate drop in the quantity of DNA that can be extracted, and whilst high molecular weight DNA is present, significant degradation has occurred. The use of propylene glycol in the solution does not appear to effect the overall preservation of the DNA in 80 per cent IMS solutions. Archival samples that had been preserved in 80 per cent IMS for over fifteen years still yielded extractable DNA, but this was significantly degraded. From this it can be deduced that the action of water is likely to be the main contributing factor to the degradation of the DNA. Thus there is evidence to suggest that although the level of denaturant additives (i.e. methyl alcohol) in IMS is low, their effect on the preservation of DNA is potentially

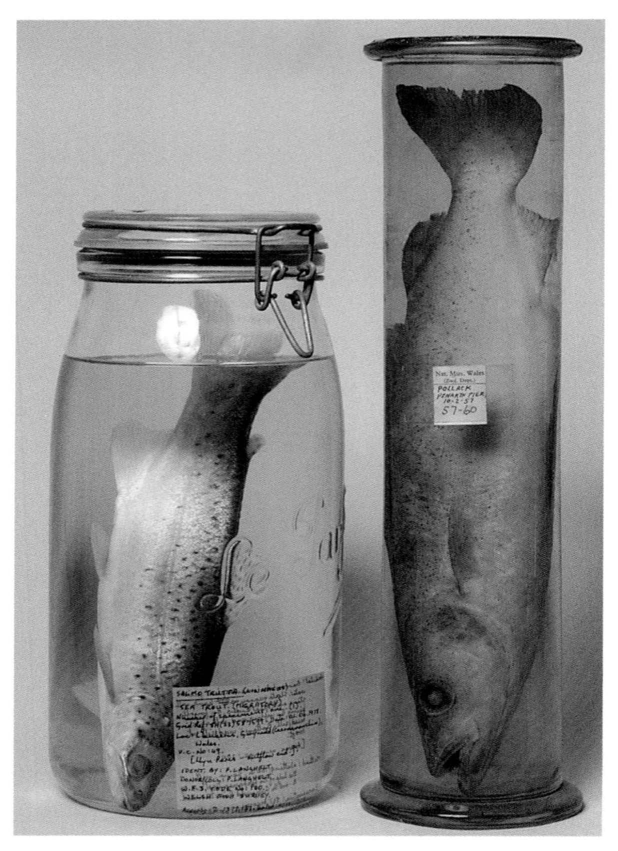

significant, especially over time. In addition the presence of water in the preserving solution will also add significantly to the degradation of the DNA

Whilst our current methods of preservation do have the potential to preserve DNA, the major problem is still that when an organism dies the cellular protection mechanisms are no longer effective. By investigating possible methods for improving fluid preservation treatments it should be possible to enhance both morphological and molecular preservation in museum preserved specimens. Current research at the National Museum of Wales is considering such factors.

In the meantime, the standard methods we use are likely to preserve DNA in a condition suitable for molecular studies, especially as the procedures used in these studies continue to improve. Our biological collections are an important resource, and their value is increased by the development of molecular analytical methods.

Julian Carter

DILLON, N., AUSTIN, A. D. & BARTOWSKY, E. 1996. Comparison of preservation techniques for DNA extraction from hymenopterous insects. *Insect Molecular Biology*, 5, 21-4.

QUICKE, D. L. J., BELSHAW, R. & LOPEZ-VAAMONDE, C. 1999. Preservation of hymenopteran specimens for subsequent molecular and morphological study. *Zoology Scripta*, 1-2, 261-7.

REISS, R. A., SCHWERT, D. P. & ASHWORTH, A. C. 1995. Field Preservation of coleoptera for molecular genetic analysis. *Environmental Entomology*, 24. 716-19.

THOMAS R. H. 1994. Analysis of DNA from natural history museum collections, 311-321. In SCHIERWATER, B., STREIT B., WAGNER G. P. & DESALLE, R. (eds). *Molecular Ecology and Evolution: Approaches and Applications.* Birkhäuser Verlag AG, Basel-Boston.

The polymerase chain reaction (PCR) and molecular analysis methods

The PCR process is driven by a unique enzyme called *Taq* DNA polymerase whose cellular function is to copy DNA. The enzyme was originally isolated from a thermophilic bacterium called *Thermus aquaticus* (aka *Taq*).
This bacterium lives in conditions of extreme heat, and as a result the *Taq* DNA polymerase is not denatured by limited exposure to temperatures as high as 95°C. The PCR process copies DNA by using the behaviour characteristics of DNA at different temperatures, and the *Taq's* ability to survive high temperatures. The DNA section to be copied is identified using specific short pieces of synthesised DNA called primers. These inform the *Taq* enzyme when to start copying a section of DNA (Hillis et al. 1996). By repeating the PCR process thirty or forty times it is possible to produce many millions of copies of the template DNA. These can be used in studies of species determination between closely related species, assessing parentage, relatedness and in analysis of population structure.

HILLIS, D. M., MORITZ, C. & MABLE, B. K. 1996. *Molecular Systematics*, 2nd Edition. Sinauer Associates, Sunderland, Massachusetts.

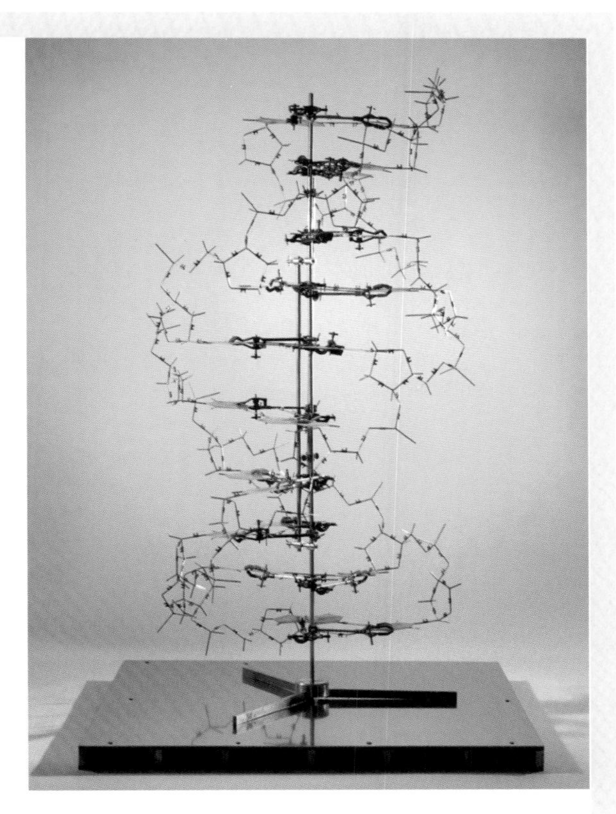

A replica of the original DNA model built by Francis Crick and James Watson in 1953
© Science Museum

Conserving a coal mine
Keeping our industrial heritage working

Top right: Big Pit when it was an active coal mine
Below right: Big Pit today

Wales was the world's first industrialised country, that is, a country where more than half the population was involved in industrial work. Although it had an ancient history in mining for metals such as gold, tin and copper, by the eighteenth and nineteenth centuries coal-mining and iron working were predominant. The parallel development of these industries was one of the key dynamic forces of the world's first industrial revolution. The south Wales valleys were transformed from an agricultural backwater to an industrial society.

The area around Blaenafon in south Wales is one of the finest surviving examples in the world of a landscape created by coal mining and iron working in the late eighteenth and early nineteenth centuries. In the late eighteenth century the ironworks were built and by 1812 they were claimed to be among the most productive in the world. In recognition of this, in December 2000, Blaenafon was designated a World Heritage Site and acknowledged as an area of outstanding universal value by UNESCO; it is the duty of the international community to co-operate to protect such sites.

In 2000, the National Museum of Wales took over the running of Big Pit, a former working coal mine in Blaenafon. The site at Big Pit is of great historical value, owing to its accessible underground workings and its above-ground complex. There are substantial conservation problems associated with preserving such a site, from the ethical considerations of the preservation versus presentation dichotomy, and the additional impositions from government listed building regulations and World Heritage Site status.

Big Pit, until its closure, was the oldest working coal mine in south Wales, dating from 1860 when the original shaft was sunk. Originally supplying coal to the adjacent Blaenafon Company ironworks, it was operated commercially by the Blaenafon Company from 1873, and was nationalised by the National Coal Board in 1947. Its value as an historical site was recognized from the early 1970s, and measures were introduced then to preserve the authenticity and integrity of the site. It also acted as a collecting area for surplus equipment from other mines as an alternative to their disposal.

On its closure in 1980, Big Pit was one of approximately forty pits still working in the south Wales area; when it was first opened to the public in 1983 it was not so much as a 'museum' but as a 'job-creating' tourist attraction (Walker 1997). However, by the early 1990s deep coal working was virtually extinct in south Wales and Big Pit's significance as the survivor of an earlier age became apparent. In recognition of this, Cadw: Welsh Historic Monuments listed many of the above-ground buildings and structures, with the rationale that 'Big Pit was the most functionally complete colliery complex remaining in South Wales'.

Big Pit became part of the National Museum of Wales as part of our industrial strategy, and became the National Coal Museum of Wales. With this take-over and concomitant grant applications to the Heritage Lottery Fund, fundamental ethical questions had to be considered on how the site should be conserved.

Preservation principles: what should we preserve?

Since the massive de-industrialisation of the 1980s and 1990s much of the structural landscape has changed. Mines have disappeared, coal tips have been flattened and grassed over and houses no longer burn coal but North Sea gas. Too much of the social and local economic landscape has gone, and it would be inappropriate to resurrect or recreate it in

Corrosion of metal
exposed to the elements

order to set the Big Pit complex in 'authentic' surroundings. The Management Guidelines for World Cultural Sites (ICCROM 1998) emphasise the criteria for consideration as ones of 'historical integrity' and 'authenticity'. They define 'authenticity' as 'original or genuine, as it was constructed and as it has aged and weathered in time, and should not be confused with "identical"; e.g. modern reconstruction'. Therefore, the Big Pit site and buildings should be preserved and maintained in their present format and not 'enhanced' with reconstructions of other 'typical' buildings. The interpretation and exhibition of the site should be based on the current contents, which represent the mine at its closure in 1980.

This viewpoint is echoed by Cadw's decision to list twelve surface structures in 1995. This prevents any destruction or alteration of the buildings without prior consent and ensures that they receive adequate and proper care and maintenance. However, as Jones (Jones 1983) notes in his discussion paper on the conservation of the coal heritage in south Wales, 'scheduling is essentially negative' and does not initiate positive measures of conservation.

Big Pit sits in an exposed situation 1,400 feet above sea level, in an area of high rainfall and bleak winters. The principal causes of deterioration of the collections are therefore moisture and high humidity, causing corrosion, paint flaking and failure of metals and rotting wood. The effects are exacerbated by general air pollution (despite its rural position), off-gassing from the coal itself, dirt and the effects of sunlight.

The argument for preservation of the site as it stands is easy to justify and has great ethical merit. More debatable is the degree of activity that should be allowed, as working machinery, visitor tours and demonstrations are a balance between preservation and active interpretation. It is self-evident that a mine complex that demonstrates how it operated when it was a working mine is more realistic and more of a visitor experience than a fossilised static exhibit. Current debate on the ethics of conservation notes the advantages of continuing to run machinery, as it aids interpretation and maintains specialist skills in the maintenance, care and repair of such machinery (Paine 1994).

How should the material be preserved?

Coal mines are part of special socio-economic areas that breed unique communities and foster particular virtues and vices. The operation of the mines in Wales developed into a traditional activity with a strong personal base. Apprentices joined a particular mine, often as boys, and developed skills and knowledge specific to their area. When these mines ceased to be active as producing industrial units, the workforce was dispersed either through redundancy and early retirement or by taking alternative jobs outside the industry. The few mines preserved as museums rely on a mix of ageing miners – usually former employees – and others who have more general experience of heavy engineering. There is a concern that, increasingly, these specialist skills and experience will be lost as the ex-employees retire and are not replaced by upcoming apprentices.

In order to maintain the concept of authenticity, we consulted widely on the future conservation of the contents of Big Pit.

First and foremost in the discussions was the point that Big Pit is classified as a working mine and perforce must conform to the requirements of the Management and Administration of Safety and Health at Mines Regulations 1993 (MASHAM) and other demanding health and safety legislation. Additionally, the licence-holder of a coal mine (nominally the owner) must abide by the extensive number of Acts of Parliament, Approved Codes of Practices and Guidance on Regulations that govern operational practices, maintenance and repair regimes, monitoring and documentation procedures. All of which are good preventative conservation measures.

The weight of coal-mining legislation makes most of our ethical decisions for us. If a 'working' mine is the favoured interpretative format, the appropriate laws must be adhered to. This approach is supported by *Guidelines to Safety in Working Museums* (Walker 1997), which takes a pragmatic view on operating machinery in heritage settings.

There is, however, a large amount of material in a coal-mining setting that is not necessarily operational and is not covered by any specific legislation, but is still vulnerable and needs conservation. Big Pit coal mine is a contextual site that achieves its relevance as an historical document of post-war industrial conditions that existed there

until its closure as a working mine in 1980.
The objects seen on a public visit to the site are the 'tools of the trade' and their traditional use, maintenance and repair by the mining workforce play an integral part of the geographical, historical and socio-economic scene. They fall into three categories (Child 1997). First, the working machinery that needs to be maintained to a legal and safe standard only by professional and trained operatives. Second, the static and unused machinery, which provides the context to the site and can be conserved by trained staff. Finally, the collections and individual items that have importance as museum objects through rarity, age or cultural value and must be conserved by qualified conservation staff.

Ethical conservation

Owing to the special nature of the Big Pit collections in the context of the site, conservation methods need to be considered with care and ethical guidelines drawn up. The overriding priority is the safety of staff and visitors. It is considered preferable to improve the environment by better drainage, ventilation and coverings rather than applying protective coatings, which may be inappropriate to the context and be visually unacceptable. Preventative conservation measures should be unobtrusive where possible, using measures such as hard-standings, good ventilation and canvas covers. Protective coatings such as grease or paint will only be used where they had some traditional use in the former working mine. If treatments are required they must be unobtrusive and, where possible, based on existing traditional methods of maintenance and repair, and preferably be carried out by local staff. 'Museum' conservation methodologies should only be used for objects in 'museum' type storage or displays, where additional conservation measures are necessary for their long-term preservation. Restoration may be necessary but only where there is a need for that object to be re-used in the mine context in a condition that better illustrates its use or appearance and its interpretation. Any restoration should use traditional crafts, techniques and standards, and be fully documented.

Preservation of the underground workings

Big Pit is a wet mine with over 100,000 gallons of water draining through it every day. Luckily, it has few problems from sulphur or methane gas emissions from the coal face itself, and so most of the problems are from very high ambient relative humidities. Being underground, the ambient temperatures are temperate at about 15°C throughout the year.

Conservation of the underground machinery can only be satisfactorily achieved with effective protective coatings. Where possible, this is being done using original and traditional materials including paint systems and grease. In some areas, to maintain an authentic appearance we are considering full paint systems but with an artificial weathering and corroded surface finish.

The underground mining areas of Big Pit were excavated over the past one hundred years both for ironstone and coal. Some of the workings are not only of interest historically, but also geologically and biologically.

We are fortunate in having departments concerned with geology and biological sciences as well as industry and commerce, and therefore monitoring and documentation of the mine workings is an ongoing exercise. As some underground areas have been inactive and unused for a long time, they are now considered in the same light as historic caves and as such are viewed according to the guidelines of the National Caving Association's Guidelines.

Future considerations

Big Pit is one of the foremost cultural heritage centres in the south Wales valleys. It attracts large numbers of local visitors, especially schoolchildren who wish to learn about their local history and its now defunct industry. Many visitors from further afield are delighted with the experience of going down 'a real coal mine with real coal miners'.

The challenge for the conservation of Big Pit is not just the preservation of its structures and machinery, but also the knowledge, experience and working practices of its workforce – a resource that without forethought and planning will die out with the last miner.

Robert Child

Left: the famous Big Pit underground tour, accompanied by a former miner

CHILD, R. E. 1997. *Ethics & conservation*, 207-215. In EDSON, G. (ed.). *Museum Ethics*. Routledge. London and New York.

ICCROM. 1998. *Management Guidelines for World Cultural Heritage Sites*. Rome.

JONES, W. D. 1983. *The Coal Mining Industry in Wales: Its Conservation, Preservation and Interpretation*. National Museum of Wales Discussion Paper. Unpublished.

PAINE, C. (ed.). 1994. *Standards in the Museum Care of Larger and Working Objects*. Museums and Galleries Commission. London.

WALKER, P. 1997. Maintenance of Working Objects at Big Pit Mining Museum, 129-137. In DOLLERY, D. & HENDERSON, J. (eds). *Industrial Collections: Care and Conservation*, Council of Museums in Wales & United Kingdom Institute of Conservation, Cardiff.

Anoxic storage

Oxygen is responsible for the majority of chemical reactions that lead to the decay and degradation of artefacts; the corrosion of metals or the fading of pigments when exposed to ultraviolet light could not occur without the presence of oxygen. Equally, it is also essential for the life forms responsible for biological decay such as insects, fungi and bacteria.

The technology to produce oxygen-free environments to museum standards has burgeoned in the last few years. Nitrogen and other inert gases such as argon and helium have been successfully used to display specimens anoxically. Anoxic storage can also now be achieved relatively cheaply and efficiently for smaller objects with the use of barrier films and oxygen scavengers.

Barrier films are multi-layered laminates, which include a gas and water vapour barrier film and a heat-sealable layer. Opaque foils, with an aluminium layer, are an excellent barrier to the transmission of water and gas. They have been used for creating microenvironments and lining display cases to protect objects from emissions from wood and fibreboard. However, transparent films are desirable for the long term storage of museum specimens, so their condition can be monitored without opening the enclosures. Transparent barrier films can be composed of a variety of materials and have a huge range of water and gas transmission rates, but until relatively recently these rates have not been good enough for long-term storage of museum objects. Some of the latest generation of transparent films, however, are made from a barrier layer of a vacuum-deposited ceramic on a PVA substrate, and these new films are proving as effective as opaque ones.

Effective oxygen absorbers designed for the food industry have been available for over ten years, and are used for pest control, low humidity microclimates, anoxic storage and display. The first readily available oxygen absorbers worked at high relative humidities within the enclosure. Whilst oxidative reactions would be halted, there was concern about subjecting specimens to such high relative humidities, especially if the enclosure failed. Microclimates in museums are commonly used for specimens that need low or specific relative humidity conditions, so these original oxygen absorbers were not suitable. The development of the RP System™ (Mitsubishi Gas Chemical Company) solved this problem. This oxygen absorber comes in two varieties: one has incorporated an inorganic desiccant so is ideal for objects requiring very low humidity conditions, the other is moisture neutral. As well as oxygen, the RP system™ also removes corrosive gases, for example sulphur dioxide, hydrogen sulphide, hydrogen chloride and ammonia.

Monitoring the levels of oxygen in the enclosure is important. Oxygen indicating tablets can be used. They are good to ensure the initial integrity of the enclosure, but they do not have as long a life as the scavenger, and

A mineral packed in an anoxic microenvironment

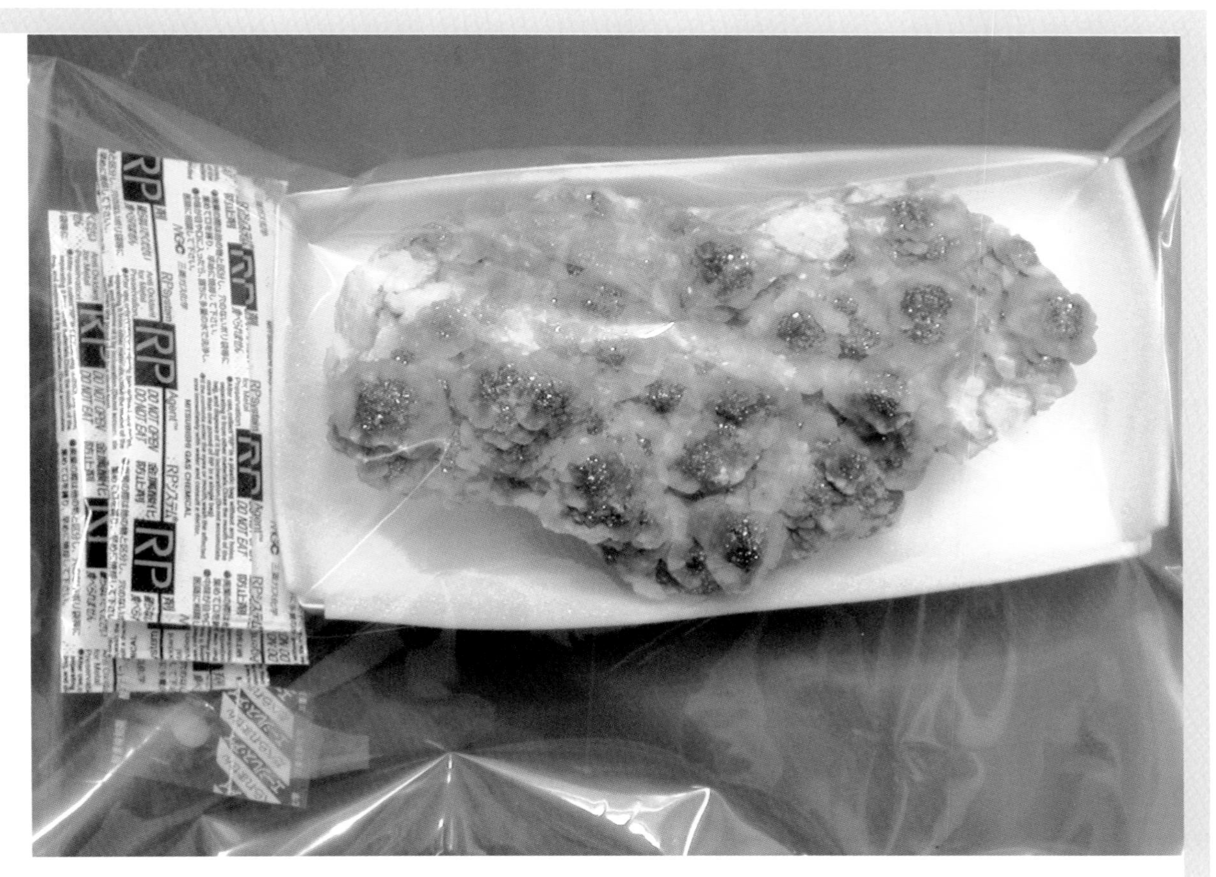

their colour will fade with time and so cannot be relied upon in the long term. Other problems can be found in the sealed environment: finite quantities of air and water vapour are present, and so the dew point will rise and fall with any temperature change. Temperature, therefore, must be anticipated when the required humidity created is to be kept stable, otherwise the package could become dry at elevated temperatures, and condensation could form when temperatures are depressed.

Interventive conservation

The conservation of the past is (also) a peculiarly modern preoccupation, born out of a vain hope that we can freeze time and the vain notion that what we are trying to freeze is the past... What we are trying to freeze is actually the present, which offers a highly distorted, fragmentary version of the past.

A. Stille, *The Future of the Past* (2002)

Preventative conservation is becoming increasingly dominant as a method of preservation, but is not always practicable or the best solution for certain problems. Sometimes correct storage and packaging, although seen as the ideal, are not sufficient to ensure the long-term survival of an object, and interventive or remedial conservation may be required. The degree of treatment will vary, starting with the minimum possible, but more may be required depending upon the condition and the future use of the object.

Interventive conservation can be undertaken for a variety of reasons; the most ethically straightforward is to stabilise an object, for either physical or chemical reasons, or both. Archaeological waterlogged organic artefacts such as wood and leather are prone to further bacterial decay when excavated, and also physical disintegration if allowed to dry out without treatment. Although such objects can be stored wet, and sometimes frozen, they are not readily accessible in such a state, nor stable under conditions which are easy to maintain. If such items are to be kept long term for study or display, they need to be conserved.

Similar situations are true for many fragile objects in diverse collections: some fossils can be too fragmentary to handle, excavated objects might still be covered in dirt and biological specimens will decay. Further study of all these types of objects would require some cleaning and stabilisation before investigative conservation or study can take place.

Although there are many non-interventive investigatory techniques such as X-radiography, it is still the case with many types of objects that remedial conservation is actually part of the examination process. It is often from this part of conservation practice that information is found out about the artefact's composition, construction and history. However, it is also understood that when undertaking remedial conservation no treatment is entirely reversible.

A further step might still be needed if the items are required for display. It is easier to keep artefacts stable in dark, cool and controlled atmospheres; but part of the function of a museum is to display its collections. Interventive conservation can help protect artefacts, for example lacquering silver coins, which are prone to tarnish, lessens the need for repeated cleaning.

Economics, as well as ethics, now mean that museums and other heritage organizations lean towards preventative conservation and collections management as the panacea for all conservation issues, without necessarily weighing up all the factors contributing towards the long-term care of artefacts. It is easier, and cheaper, to put a newly excavated object in a box and let it 'restabilise' to specific storage conditions in a museum; but reactions are possibly occurring under the drying soil that in the future could be far more difficult to remove; information could be lost, and certainly overlooked. Some conservation practices of the recent past are now seen as a luxury, but over-simplifying the care of artefacts by passive means could be detrimental in the long term.

Good conservation practice using a balanced combination of preventative and interactive stabilisation is necessary, and the diminishing role of interventive conservation means an important skill base is being reduced.

Underground, overground
Reconstructing the Caerleon sarcophagus

During the excavation of foundations for an extension to the Gwent College of Higher Education in November 1995, workmen cut through a stone object deep within one of their trenches. Although there were no visible archaeological features in that particular area, it had long been known that there was a Roman cemetery within the general locality, near to the Legionary Fortress of Isca (Caerleon). At first, the workmen thought they had cut through a box drain made up of sandstone blocks, but closer investigation revealed the remains of a skeleton within the stone-lined chamber. Work was stopped and archaeologists were called to supervise the excavation of the remains (Fox 1996).

Careful excavation of the rest of the stone feature and the retrieval of the material that had already been unearthed by the mechanical digger revealed a near-complete but highly fragmented Bath stone sarcophagus with its lid. It contained one skeleton and grave goods in the form of a small glass flask (unguentarium) and a shale bowl. The sarcophagus fragments, skeletal remains and grave-goods were taken to the Roman Legion Museum at Caerleon for study and conservation.

Up until this point, only various forms of cremation burial had been represented and displayed in the museum at Caerleon. Cremation was the dominant burial rite practised by Romanised people up until about AD 150, after which there was a gradual change towards inhumation burials (Boon 1972). From a curatorial perspective the sarcophagus was an obvious candidate for reconstruction and display. It would fill the gap in our representation of burial practices in Roman Britain and demonstrate changes in ideas and beliefs associated with the development of different burial practices during this period. The decision to proceed with reconstruction and display was further supported by radiocarbon dates from the skeleton that indicated a date around AD 200 for the burial. This suggests that the sarcophagus dates to the transitional phase or not long afterwards. As the empire had expanded to incorporate new races and cultures, there became a greater movement of people and ideas. Locally, historic beliefs, customs and practices assimilated new ideas, especially from the East.

The terms 'coffin' and 'sarcophagus' have slightly different meanings. A coffin is a container within which a body is placed for burial, usually made of lead or wood, and the term coffin is thought to derive from the Old French *cofin* meaning a chest or

Left: a section through the sarcophagus as it was first revealed by a mechanical digger on the building site

Top: excavation of the sarcophagus at the site

Below: arranging and drawing the stone fragments

from the Greek *kophinos* (Latin *cophinus*) meaning basket. In this instance the body appeared to have been placed directly within the stone receptacle, with no evidence for an internal coffin of wood or lead. The word sarcophagus comes from the Greek *sarx* (flesh) and *phago* (I eat). The word sarcophagus therefore means 'flesh-eater', and was derived through the notion that the stone used to a create sarcophagus had properties that digested the body within a few weeks of deposition.

The sarcophagus before conservation

Right: The sarcophagus after conservation, with the skeleton and grave goods

Conservation of the sarcophagus

A specialist stone conservator, Paul Giudici, was employed to undertake the conservation of the sarcophagus, and initial discussions concerning display, conservation and curation were set up before any work proceeded. The proposed design comprised a plinth for the sarcophagus with a toughened glass plate to seal the sarcophagus and to take the larger lid fragments. The remains of the skeleton and the grave-goods could be placed on display within the sarcophagus and viewed through the toughened glass. The Bath stone had a very tactile and textured surface; it was felt that this could best be appreciated by leaving the sides of the sarcophagus unenclosed by glass.

Bath stone is a coarse grained limestone which was probably quarried in Roman times from an area around Bath. It is made up mainly of spherical particles called ooliths, which grew in shallow, warm, Jurassic seas as accretions of calcite around small nuclei of shell and rock fragments; calcite is highly susceptible to attack by weak acids. All rain is slightly acidic because it picks up a small amount of carbon dioxide from the atmosphere to form a weak carbonic acid. This results in acidic burial conditions where the ground is free draining, as with the location of this sarcophagus which was found on a steep free-draining slope overlooking Caerleon.

Comparisons between the outer and inner surfaces of the sarcophagus clearly indicate dissolution of the stone which has left an undulating outer surface, especially at the top of the lid. In some areas this has resulted in 'solution-holes' penetrating through the entire width of the stone lid. The damage to the exterior surfaces of the sarcophagus, including the solution holes, is the result of percolating groundwater through the soil on top of the sarcophagus.

The physical properties of Bath stone are also notably altered when it is damp or wet, and this has long been a well-known phenomenon for this type of stone. Bath stone mined today is left to dry before being used, during which time it hardens.

At the time of excavation, the stone was very damp, and appeared seriously damaged. Upon initial inspection it was felt that the sarcophagus retained very little physical integrity or cohesive strength. It had been stored for some time outside and under tarpaulins. When we examined it to assess its conservation needs, it was extremely soft and friable, with lichen and moss growing on the surface. Brushing the surface at this point in time would brush away a layer of soft crumbly stone along with any dirt. The conservators were sceptical at first as to whether the reconstructed sarcophagus would be able to support itself without strengthening and consolidating the stone. However, the outside storage under a tarpaulin had allowed very little air movement around the stone, which had remained

The shale bowl, after conservation

inherently damp. The stone conservator's first advice before considering what type of treatment to undertake was to get it inside, and into a well ventilated area so it could slowly dry out. As with the newly quarried stone, this made an enormous difference.

The porosity of Bath stone means that the presence of any soluble salts within the stone matrix could cause problems as the stone dried. As water is lost, solutions containing salts will crystallise out within the stone which can cause the stone to crack or spall. The sarcophagus fragments were carefully monitored during indoor drying, and there was no evidence of crystallising salts as they dried. This outcome is consistent with burial in a free-draining deposit where the rainfall exceeds evaporation.

Slow drying hugely strengthened the sarcophagus making it possible to proceed with the reconstruction without consolidation. The sarcophagus fragments had been lightly washed upon discovery and transfer to the Museum in 1995. Now all broken surfaces were cleaned to maximise the closeness and strength of joins; this was done by surface dry brushing and vacuuming.

The sarcophagus fragments were next strapped together; this was essential for maintaining the accuracy of the joins within a three-dimensional and slightly asymmetric object. It also allowed accurate measurements of the sarcophagus and an estimate of its final weight to be made for the first time.

Reconstruction was conducted using corrosion resistant stainless steel fixings dowels set into drilled holes with a polyester resin. Areas of missing stone were not gap-filled, partly so people could see into the interior of the sarcophagus through the holes in the sides, but also as they were not necessary to support the structure of the sarcophagus. It was felt that gap-filling in this instance would amount to over-restoration for this type of object and display. Access to the skeleton and artefacts within the sarcophagus through the gaps was prevented by a polyamide insert, lining the inside of the sarcophagus.

Contents of the sarcophagus

As much of the skeleton as possible was recovered from the site, though some remained lost or damaged. The slight acidity of the soil which had caused the softening and degradation of the stone sarcophagus in the ground had also caused the dissolution of the mineral component of the bone. This meant that the bone was softened, then smashed and splintered into relatively small pieces and had to be recovered from what was, in effect, now building site debris.

The remains of the skeleton were sent to the pathology laboratories at Bristol University, where they were examined; and it was there that the

The sarcophagus, now on display at the National Roman Legion Museum

majority of the skull was reconstructed. Only minor modifications to this initial reconstruction were carried out later in the conservation laboratory. The individual was thought to be a man, probably aged between thirty and forty years old. Fragments from many areas of the skeleton had been found, including bones from the hands, feet, spine, pelvis and limbs. However the vast majority of these were broken and incomplete and it was therefore not possible to estimate the man's height.

Two artefacts were also found within the debris that had been buried with the body. The first of these consisted of several minute shards and the neck of a small glass vessel. Many fragments were missing – which made an accurate reconstruction of the vessel impossible. Shapes of some of the shards, especially at the neck of the vessel give an indication of its original form, which was probably a small rounded flask with a long neck.

The final object recovered was also fragmented, although several pieces were retrieved. This was the remains of a shale bowl, which had not fractured or splintered as much as the skeleton or the glass. The bowl was found in five relatively large fragments. One piece retained the whole of the base – which had been skilfully turned on a lathe to produce a succession of concentric circles; two of the smaller fragments were from the rim. All the fragments were stored damp in a refrigerator, still covered by the mud they were found in, until the conservation work was undertaken.

There are several problems with conserving archaeological shale. The shiny black pristine looking fragments which are recovered from waterlogged or damp sites, partly owe their appearance to 'unbound' water bonded to the layers of hydrophilic clay which form part of the structure of the shale. When the object dries, and this water is lost, often a whole series of laminar cracks will start to appear, and the shale often begins to look grey or brown rather than black. In some cases the whole object can disintegrate. It is very difficult to predict the degree of degradation that has occurred during the life and burial of an artefact, and several methods of treatment have been used over the last thirty years with varying degrees of success. Unfortunately, this is not the type of material which occurs naturally in quantity in archaeological contexts so it has been very difficult to undertake objective studies of its treatment.

Most treatments try to replace the water with another material that will stay in situ when the object has dried. This has been done using water soluble waxes (such as polyethylene glycol) (Oddy & Lane 1976) or by 'dewatering' the material by substituting the water with organic solvents, and then consolidating the object with resins dissolved within those solutions. It is hoped the resin will remain within the cracks and voids of the shale when the solvent has evaporated and so prevent delamination and spalling of the stone.

The bowl was initially washed in water and then soaked – as in previous treatments – in a high grade polyethylene glycol. Although this wax is solid at room temperature, it can be dissolved in water. Initially the bowl was placed in a dilute solution, but the concentration was gradually increased over a period of two months. This is a method of consolidation that had been tried in the past with variable levels of success; it was therefore decided that the drying stage should be modified in the hope of improving the final outcome of the treatment. It was felt that by leaving the object to air dry, the surface tension caused by the evaporation of 'unbound' water could cause further stresses on the vulnerable surface of the shale. We therefore decided to try and bypass this problematic stage, as with the conservation of many organic materials, and to freeze dry the bowl.

The results of the freeze drying were mostly good; a crack which was just visible within the largest fragment before treatment opened up slightly more when dry; and some of the surface had developed a fine crazing. However, the dimensions of the bowl fragments had remained undistorted through the drying process, which allowed them to be glued together easily, and extensive delamination had not occurred.

Excess (white-coloured) polyethylene glycol was removed from the surface, and the bowl was further protected with a layer of microcrystalline wax. The bowl was then conditioned in the laboratory so it could adjust to a stable temperature and relative humidity which was similar to that within the Roman Legion Museum.

Displaying the sarcophagus

Ethical issues regarding the display of human remains and associated artefacts were considered. In May 2001 the UK Government launched a working group to look into the legal status, retention and use of human remains and associated artefacts in UK museums (Working Group on Human Remains in Museum Collections [HRWG]). The findings of this inquiry were not known during the planning stages of the sarcophagus's display. It was felt that as long as the sarcophagus and the human remains were exhibited in the gallery in a wholly educational manner its display would be acceptable and respectful of the scientific and archaeological value of the remains. The government working group reported in November 2003; this was an independent advisory committee, so its report was to form the basis of a consultation document rather than reflect government policy at that time. At the time of writing this consultation document from the Department for Media, Culture and Sport is still awaited, but the working group report upheld the aim to respect the sanctity and scientific value of human remains. It was noted that more than two-thirds of the English museums consulted currently displayed human remains.

The sarcophagus and its contents were put on permanent display in the air-conditioned gallery of the Roman Legion Museum, Caerleon in July 2002. To date no complaints regarding the display of human remains have been received. School parties visiting the Museum at Caerleon are now routinely given a talk about the displays, which includes discussing the sensitivities of displaying human remains and appropriate behaviour in the gallery.

The result of these introductory sessions has been very noticeable; all the exhibits within the gallery, including items on open display, have been treated with much more respect. The sarcophagus is clearly one of the Museum's most popular exhibits with all ages.

Mark Lewis and Mary Davis

Report of the Working Group on Human Remains. 2003. Department for Media, Culture and Sport.

BOON, G. C. 1972. *Isca*. National Museum of Wales, Cardiff.

FOX, S. A. 1996. Caerleon, Gwent College of Higher Education: Rathmell Extension, 54. In EVANS, E. (ed.). *Archaeology in Wales* Volume 35, 1995.

MORRIS, J. 2003. Dead but not buried. *Museums Journal* December 2003, 12-13.

ODDY, W. A. & LANE, H. 1976. The Conservation of Waterlogged Shale. *Studies in Conservation*, 21, 63-66.

Shale

Shale is a general term for a fine grained sedimentary rock formed underwater by the consolidation of silt and clay. It is finely bedded and tends to split along planar surfaces. Mineralogically the composition can be varied, but commonly consists of clay minerals, detrital quartz, feldspar and mica. Clays contain a certain amount of 'bound' water that remains bonded to the clay molecules (unless they are heated to several hundred degrees), but the clay also potentially attracts a large amount of 'unbound' water. This can cause swelling and deformation of shale as the water is taken up in wet conditions and lost in drier conditions.

Shales that contain a relatively high percentage of organic matter are often referred to as 'oil shales' or 'bituminous shales' (the correct geological term is sapropelite). They formed in anoxic conditions which led to the preservation of organic matter within the shale, for example Jurassic aged Kimmeridge Shale. It is the organic component of these oil shales that makes them relatively easy to work and gives shale artefacts their characteristic black shiny finish. Kimmeridge Shale has been used for many thousands of years for the production of black ornaments and decorative items. In Roman times the shale was turned on a lathe to produce a large number of artefacts including table legs, bangles and bowls.

Iron sulphide, also known as pyrite, is a relatively common inclusion within shales and this can cause major problems for conservators (see *Pyrite decay* p.159). The correct environmental storage conditions are imperative for the long term care of shale and shale artefacts. Relative humidity below 30 per cent could cause irreparable and irreversible damage through delamination and cracking, whereas a relative humidity above 60 per cent could well promote oxidation of the pyrite within susceptible material. Widely fluctuating relative humidities have been shown to cause the most severe damage of all.

The base of the shale bowl found with the sarcophagus

Freeze drying

Waterlogged archaeological material can present enormous conservation problems.

Organic material will normally completely degrade and rot away in temperate climates in aerated soils, but does occasionally survive where it has been buried in waterlogged conditions. This is where the environment lacks oxygen and so the majority of normal biological decay is slowed down or halted; only a minority of the bacteria and fungi responsible for decomposition can live in anaerobic conditions.

In the case of material such as wood, this often means that much of the softer tissue will have been lost, but some of the structural elements such as the lignin will remain intact. The cell walls will have lost much of their strength, but their three-dimensional character and shape are retained as long as these spaces are filled with water. When this water is lost the result is catastrophic to the object. Decayed structures have little resistance to the high surface tension exerted by water, which, when it evaporates, literally leaves a vacuum behind it, causing the structure to collapse and the object to shrink and distort. The collapsed cell walls will then bond to one another making it impossible to rehydrate the object back into its former shape.

Freeze drying avoids this damage to organic materials by removing the water without it entering its liquid phase.

The two major factors that determine whether a substance is a solid, liquid or gas are heat and atmospheric pressure. Although at ambient temperatures and pressure water is a liquid, by reducing the temperature it can be turned to ice, and by reducing the pressure it can be converted into water vapour. Freeze-drying works by freezing the objects and then using a very low pressure to sublime water molecules directly from ice to vapour.

The material can be pre-treated with substances such as polyethylene glycol or glycerol, which can have various functions, acting as bulking agents, anti-freezes, lubricants and humectants. The object is first frozen in a freezer or in the freeze-drier chamber. The chamber is then sealed and a vacuum pulled; this forces air out, and so lowers the atmospheric pressure in the chamber. A small amount of heat is then added to the system, causing the ice to change phase, but as the pressure is so low it converts directly from ice into vapour. The water vapour is pulled from the chamber by the vacuum into a colder chamber, where it condenses as ice. The drying process can be monitored by regularly weighing the object; when the weight remains steady, the process is complete.

Although we primarily use freeze drying for treating waterlogged archaeological material such as wood and leather, it is now being increasingly employed to preserve small mammals such as shrews and mice, as well as birds, and so avoid the need for taxidermy in these cases. It has also been used successfully to preserve plants and flowers.

A further use for freeze driers is in response to major floods or fires: many objects, especially books, can be dried out rapidly and effectively, limiting the degree of damage resulting from water.

Freeze dried zoological specimens

Buy one get one free
Turner's *Llandeilo Bridge and Dynevor Castle*

Five days after the sale of J. M. W. Turner's *Llandeilo Bridge and Dynevor Castle* at Sotheby's in 1938, A. M. Hind, the keeper of prints and drawings at the British Museum, wrote to the director of the National Museum of Wales, Sir Cyril Fox. Hind identified the work as the '*Llandilo Bridge and Dinevor Castle*' Turner had exhibited at the Royal Academy in 1796 and noted that although the British Museum 'believed it to be a genuine early Turner', they had only bid up to the moderate price of £30 'as we have so much Turner'. He now advised Fox to purchase it from the successful bidder, the Palser Gallery of St James's, who had bought it for £40. David Baxandall, then Assistant Keeper of Art, enthusiastically endorsed Hind's suggestion, and the watercolour was purchased for £55. The following year, Baxandall contrasted it with two other Welsh watercolours by Turner in the Museum's collection: *Marford Mill* exhibited at the RA in 1795 and *Ewenny Priory*, exhibited in 1797:

It shows the transition from objectivity to subjectivity actually in progress. The regard for the reality of the objects depicted is still present. But the picture as a whole has another interest, for this carefully delineated bridge is set in an effect of light that made its own poetic appeal to the artist. (Baxandall 1939)

Probably on account of the intrusive discoloration of the sky, critical opinion of the watercolour remained lukewarm until its inclusion in the exhibition *Turner in Wales* in 1984.
In the accompanying catalogue, Wilton observed:

In its sumptuous evocation of evening light this water-colour is, with the Ewenny, the climax of his work based on the 1795 tour and its depiction of the castle (shown much closer than in reality) against a brilliant low sun anticipates his later preoccupation with such subjects at Cilgerran and Norham. (Wilton 1984)

As part of the ongoing programme of conservation and redocumentation of our prints and drawings collection, *Llandeilo Bridge and Dynevor Castle* came into the paper conservation studio in March 1993. Its condition was generally very discoloured, with a large area in the centre that was extremely blotchy due to an attack of mould in the past. Some small patches in the sky were abraded as if the surface of the paper had been scraped, possibly to erase localised foxing. The drawing was laid down on a supporting paper, which in turn was stuck to a similar weight paper. The last paper was badly damaged, having been partially removed around the edges and badly skinned in the centre. The mould stains were even more severe on the verso of the support papers, and it was decided to remove these in order to float wash the original watercolour. This treatment was intended to limit further degradation of the paper by removing harmful acidity and to enhance the image by reducing the brown discoloration.

When a test to determine the best method of separating the backing sheets was carried out, the adhesive (which was identified as starch) loosened on being moistened slowly with water, but it was found that the lifted edge of the second sheet carried definite brushstrokes of watercolour pigment. This indicated that a second painting might be present, making it necessary to remove the backing paper in its entirety. This was achieved by placing two layers of thick blotting paper, cut to size and lightly dampened with water, on the reverse of the drawings and leaving the package under plate glass for three hours to allow the adhesive to moisten and swell. When the work of separation began, it was

The watercolour before treatment

The discovered watercolour

A detail of the verso of the watercolour

found that water vapour, generated by an ultrasonic humidifier heated to 21°C, speeded the release of the adhesive bond, especially around the edges where previous framing techniques had left a narrow border of animal glue. The papers separated very cleanly, except for the central area where mould attack had severely weakened the structure of the paper, causing some delamination of the fibres. When the papers had been separated, they were laid side by side and the two images were compared.

It was immediately apparent that they depicted the same scene, although the shape and angle of the bridge arches differ and the castle was not included on the backing sheet. The newly discovered image is very different in technique. It appears that work began in a methodical way, with careful pencil drawing detailing the position and structure of the bridge. A light wash was laid evenly for the sky and the same pigment was used more intensely for the river where the reflections in the water were defined from the first brush-strokes. The pigment applied to the stone arches is quite dense, but precise. However, in the top right quarter of the drawing, the artist suddenly seems to have changed gear. There is an area at the base of the hill worked in small specks of indigo over a wash of yellow ochre; at first sight these appear to be dabs from thumb or finger prints, but under magnification it can be seen that the dots are too even and regular, suggesting that the pigment was applied with some type of engraving tool. Traces of pink and yellow washes can be seen under the indigo of the hill, where the final colour was briskly scrubbed on with a well-loaded brush in short looped strokes. Some particles of this thickly applied pigment were subsequently disturbed during the pasting out of the adhesive, which was done with vertical brushstrokes, so that they have offset in streaks onto the verso of the top drawing to form a strong bond. This indicates that the pigment might not have been fully dry when pasted and suggests that Turner himself stuck the sheets of paper together as part of a working process.

Further remedial conservation work was suspended until the questions raised by this discovery had been fully explored. After these investigations were complete, the remainder of the third support paper was removed. Both drawings were washed by being laid on sheets of blotting paper that had been saturated with tap water, in order to draw out the soluble acid and degraded cellulose by capillary action. This method was continued, with many changes of blotters, until no further discolouration leeched out. On drying, it was noticeable that the handling strength of the papers had increased and there was a visual improvement, particularly to the upper drawing where the delicate yellow washes above the river had again become discernible. Because of the weakened state of the papers, much discussion took place as to whether to pursue treatment solely for the visual benefits. It was considered that this was unnecessary for the uncovered image, but was worth the compromise of paper strength for exhibition work. The sky area was sprayed with a solution of hydrogen peroxide, pH corrected with ammonium hydroxide to remove the staining. However, some stains proved persistent and responded only slightly, so the treatment was abandoned after two sprays, and the drawing was rinsed thoroughly. Both drawings were then pressed and inlaid into an esparto paper support joined by strips of Japanese tissue before being remounted.

The absence of any known preparatory sketch for *Llandeilo Bridge and Dynevor Castle* may be relevant to his adoption of this unusual practice. Turner first

The watercolour after treatment

visited Llandeilo in 1795 on a tour planned to cover most places of interest in south Wales. The recently discovered drawing may have been the preliminary study, although it is impossible to prove that even the pencil underdrawing was done on the spot. Turner was to return to exactly the same viewpoint to make another sketch on his tour of 1798. It was not unusual for him to update sketchbooks on subsequent visits, since he regarded them as a valuable source of reference and often used a sketch made years earlier as the foundation for a major work. It is unlikely that he would have used the preparatory drawing to work up the final version and then considered it redundant, useful only in the sandwich of backing sheets. It is more plausible that the superimposition of the two drawings of the same view reveal a deliberate intention.

Turner was twenty-one when he exhibited this work, and it is one of the earliest examples of what became the principal and enduring preoccupation of his career – the effects of light, whether from an unclouded sun at dawn or dusk, or during more transient weather on sky, water or land. The pathos of the broken bridge and its traffic is intensified by the foreground figures washing beside the uprooted tree and by the magnified scale of the hill with the castle on top, but the main impact is the strong shaft of light cast diagonally down the slope by the semi-circle of the sun setting behind the wooded cliff. As the foreground interest is painted in muted shades of brown, the blue mass of the hill predominates, as it does in the newly discovered image, though, in this instance, the fine overall control of the brushwork continues and defines the contours and trees with the colour changing to green in the sunlit area.

Turner was to extend the parameters of many of the established watercolour techniques in his quest to convey the excitement of what he saw in nature onto a sheet of paper. Before painting these works, he had been experimenting with the process of transparencies (Bower 1990). There are two examples in the Turner Bequest (Clore, Tate Britain) where he painted indigo and black on to the verso of the sheet, so that the image on the recto is transformed when held in front of a light source. When the two *Llandeilo Bridge* drawings are superimposed as found and placed over transmitted light no comparable transformation occurs, but it can be seen that the sun in the upper sheet fits exactly over the hollowed indentation of the hill of the lower drawing. No pigment was applied to the semi-circular area on the upper sheet and the lack of a surrounding tidemark suggests the use of a stopping-out agent. The paper has been slightly thinned in this area, possibly by the removal of this resist agent, rather than actual abrasion, before the fibres were lightly burnished down.

This work may constitute an experiment with reflected rather than transmitted light using the inherent translucency of the papers. When light is shone at the surface of the superimposed drawings, it penetrates the burnished area and, to a lesser extent, the lightly pigmented areas depicting sun rays on the upper sheet before it is reflected back from the second sheet. Such lighting intensifies the brightness of the sinking sun and creates a delicate suffusion radiating from the sky over the water to enhance the yellow of the wispy clouds, while the shaft cast over the wooded flank gains depth as the light reflects back from the dark indigo. To achieve this effect, the light source has to be quite powerful and possibly more intense than any available in Turner's day, but the reflection from the underlying paper in the unpigmented areas would certainly have been more marked when the papers were new and a pristine off-white, further reinforced by a third white paper.

Prior to the discovery of this drawing, the earliest examples recognized as Turner's experiments with reflected light and the translucence of paper were the *Norham Castle* series of 1798 (Bower 1990). There is a similarity in composition – a hilltop castle defending a bend in the river and a low sun flooding the scene with sharply focused golden light. In the Norham series, the light over the landscape comes from the sun at the beginning rather than towards the end of the day. Although the method varies, in that the pigment was washed directly on the verso of these works before backing them with a plain white paper, the purpose and the result seem comparable.

These transparencies, the *Llandeilo Bridge* drawings and the *Norham Castle* group appear to be a consecutive series of experiments spanning the years from 1794 to 1798, in which Turner explored the possibilities of enriching an image by additional work behind the sheet of paper. In following the pattern, it may be pertinent that these years also saw his growing competence as a painter in oils. As he become more confident with the greater scope this medium allows in varying the opacity of superimposed layers of pigment to enhance the level of reflected light, he may have been prompted to seek a parallel method in watercolour by using washes with more power than a conventional glaze separated by a thin paper membrane.

If one of the purposes of these unusual techniques was to create watercolours that would stand comparison to oil paintings in exhibition conditions, he was not discouraged by the apparent lack of critical notice at the Royal Academy showing of *Llandeilo Bridge and Dynevor Castle*. There is no record of the original purchaser, but details of commissions listed in the south Wales sketchbook note that 'Aberdillias Mill' had been ordered by 'Mr Mitchell', it was to be 'the size of Landilio Bridge'. (Wilton 1984). Two years later, the work exhibited from the Norham Castle series, *Norham Castle on the Tweed, Summer's Morn* received much praise, with one critic saying that it had 'the force and harmony of oil painting. It is charmingly finished and the effect is both bold and natural. In short, we think it the best Landscape in the present Exhibition' (Finsberg 1961).

Christine Mackay

BAXANDALL, D. K. 1939. *The British watercolour school: Handbook to the Pyke Thompson Gallery*, Cardiff.

BOWER, P. 1990. *Turner's papers*. Exhibition catalogue. Tate Gallery, London.

FINSBERG, A. J. 1961. *The Life of J.M.W. Turner*. Clarendon Press, Oxford.

WILTON, A. 1984. *Turner in Wales*. Exhibition catalogue. Oriel Mostyn, Llandudno.

The structure of a work on paper
Most works on paper are drawn, printed or painted on a support of paper, card or occasionally parchment. Cotton, linen, hemp, straw and a variety of other cellulose fibres have been used for papermaking over the centuries, more often by recycling waste products such as old rags, sailcloth and sacking than by using fibres directly from the plant. Until the beginning of the nineteenth century, all paper was hand-made by dipping an oblong sieve into a suspension of broken-down fibres in water and then allowing the excess water to drain off. The earlier sieves or 'moulds' were made of closely spaced wires supported by thicker wires at right angles, which gives a distinctive pattern of 'laid' and 'chain lines'. In the late eighteenth century a wire mesh mould was introduced which imparted a more even structure to the sheet of paper. The first machine to use webbed cylinders making endless rolls was introduced in 1806 and the increased demand for all sorts of paper and board led to ground woodpulp becoming the main ingredient.

A newly made sheet of paper is like blotting paper and has to be 'sized' before use to prevent the inks or paints from bleeding into the fibres. Traditionally gelatine was used, with each sheet being dipped into a tub and then hung up to dry. Nowadays, the size, usually an alkyl ketene dimer, is added during the making.

The rags of handmade papers were bleached in the sun and made with the purest of water to achieve a white sheet, but chemical bleaches and optical brighteners are now employed. Kaolin, chalk and starch may also be added as fillers. Smalt was the earliest colourant for a blue paper, but as commercially produced pigments such as Prussian Blue and French Ultramarine became available they were substituted.

Because of its organic nature, paper is inherently vulnerable. It is susceptible to degradation by light, particularly ultraviolet rays, by changes in humidity, biological attacks, atmospheric pollutants, acidic storage or framing materials and handling damage. Papers made during the last 200 years can deteriorate far quicker than the older 'rag' papers, because of the use of chemically bleached, acidic wood fibres.

Drawing media include pencil (graphite), charcoal (burnt twigs), chalks (coloured earths), pastels (dry, powdered pigments bound in gum), crayon (pigments mixed with an oily, fatty or waxy binder) and various types of inks. Iron gall ink made from tannin (oak galls), vitriol (iron sulphate), gum and water was the most widely used ink until the twentieth century, with most households making their own.

Printing inks are a blend of coloured pigments or dyes with a resin or varnish binder and a solvent. The pigments are obtained from the same organic or inorganic sources as watercolours but, because of the protection given by the resin binder, are more stable. A picture printed with coloured inks will be more lightfast than one coloured by hand using watercolour.

Painting on paper is usually done with watercolour or gouache. Watercolours are made of a pigment and a binder, usually gum Arabic, with water only being important as the carrier from brush to paper; the more water used, the thinner and more translucent the resulting wash. Opaque white pigments or chalk can be mixed with watercolours to make bodycolour or gouache. Some artists also use oil paints on paper or board.

Material witness
Investigating an early medieval textile

Relatively few archaeological textiles survive from Britain, and when they do they are usually very fragile and incomplete. It is extremely rare to discover any textile from the early medieval period and this decorated piece of such high quality gives a glimpse of technologies, skills and fashions only occasionally encountered.

In 1990 a waterlogged textile was discovered during the excavation of a crannog (or man-made island) near Brecon in south-east Wales. Excavations by the National Museum of Wales and the School of History and Archaeology at Cardiff University had revealed that the crannog was a royal site of the ruler of the early medieval kingdom of Brycheiniog (Redknap & Lane 1994). The crannog was carefully constructed of brushwood and sandstone boulders, reinforced and surrounded by several lines of oak plank palisade. As a royal site the Llangorse crannog would have been a centre of administration, as well as a place for hospitality, where the ruler received tribute and indulged in hunting and fishing. The high quality of the objects found shows the aristocratic status of the inhabitants. Dendrochronological dating showed that the crannog was constructed in the 890s AD, and that it was destroyed by fire early in the tenth century.

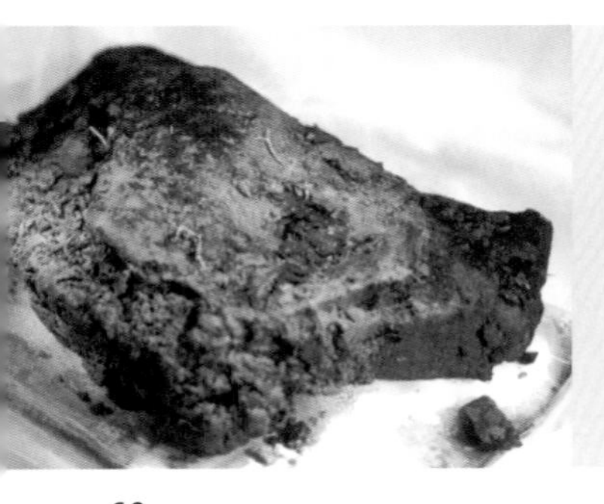

The lump of textile as excavated, before conservation.

The crannog in Llangorse Lake (Crown copyright: Royal Commission on the Ancient and Historical Monuments of Wales)

The Anglo-Saxon Chronicle for the year 916 records that a Mercian army stormed 'Brecanenmere' (thought to be the crannog) and captured 'the wife of the king and 33 other persons'.

The soil of the crannog proved to be saturated with water, with little or no air in its structure. The soil micro-organisms that have the ability to break down organic materials such as wood, leather and textile quickly are unable to operate in such an environment, and these materials can survive, albeit in a fragile, discoloured and partially degraded condition. On the crannog, there was excellent preservation of the palisade timbers and wattle fencing, and several tiny fragments of textile were recovered during sieving of the sediments. The main textile was discovered in waterlogged silts outside the north palisade, where it formed a compact lump approximately 22 x 13.5 x 6.5 cm in size, resting on a piece of charred wood.

Waterlogged archaeological materials irreversibly shrink and collapse if allowed to dry out, and so the textile was carefully packed in an airtight container and taken to the Museum for analysis and conservation. Once in the laboratory, the textile was stored in a refrigerator when not actively being worked on, since this slows down further biodeterioration. This process of decay was previously halted by the waterlogged burial environment, but could have resumed once the artefact was excavated and exposed to the air.

Examination

To examine the textile, the upper surface and sides of the lump were given a preliminary cleaning, using deionised water and soft brushes. The textile was found as a ragged bundle that had been folded in half; it was made up of more than thirty layers, which it was estimated would open up into approximately a square metre of preserved fabric. Many small roots could be seen amongst the weave, and several large hollow reeds had penetrated the bundle, making holes up to a centimetre in diameter.

Remarkably, parts of the surface of the textile appeared to be patterned in a manner resembling tapestry; the ground textile was entirely covered with tiny stitches arranged in complicated patterns. In addition, there were seams covered with minute braids and other constructional details. It was obvious that there was much information to be gained from this object. However, to obtain this it would be necessary to separate the many layers and to clean them, since the silt that permeated the weave largely obscured the very fine detail. Keeping the textile permanently wet would make study, display and storage difficult, therefore it would need to be dried.

Conservators sometimes face a conflict between obtaining information from an object and ensuring its long-term stability, and this is particularly true of waterlogged textiles. (Brooks et al 1996). To help decide on a plan for the conservation of the textile, tests were run on small, unattached pieces found in the soil around it. Examination under the Scanning Electron Microscope (SEM) revealed that the braids, sewing threads and some of the pattern threads were silk, whilst other pattern threads and the ground textile were linen. The fibres remained black and opaque even after bleaching, indicating that they were charred or incompletely burnt. It was to this charring that the textile owed its survival, since without it plant fibres such as linen are usually destroyed in the acid conditions of waterlogged soils; unfortunately, the charring also meant that any traces of dyes had been destroyed.

A textile of this size and quality is extremely rare; its analysis would undoubtedly provide valuable technological and cultural information of a type not often available to archaeologists (Mumford & Redknap 1998). After consultation with the excavator and textile historians, it was decided that unwrapping the bundle of textile should go ahead, that it should be cleaned as much as possible without damage and air-dried without a consolidant. The result would be extremely fragile, and it seemed unlikely that a mounting solution could be found that would both protect the textile and make it accessible for study. If access to the textile in the future was to be limited, then documentation would have to 'act as a surrogate object' (Textile Conservation Centre 1991); it would need to be recorded, photographed and published in such a way that every stitch was clearly visible.

Part of the design on the textile, photographed in raking light

Conservation

Before the textile could be unfolded, it had to be removed from the wood on which it had been resting. A supporting structure was moulded for the upper surface using lightweight fibreglass casting tape, with a separating layer of cling film overlaid with damp, acid-free tissue. If the entire assemblage had been inverted, the weight of the timber would have crushed the textile; fortunately there was a 2 cm-layer of silt between the textile and the wood, making it possible to slide a thin sheet of metal between the two and separate them. The bundle of textile could then be inverted, and the underside cleaned.

Once the underside had been cleaned, it became apparent that unfolding it would not be as simple

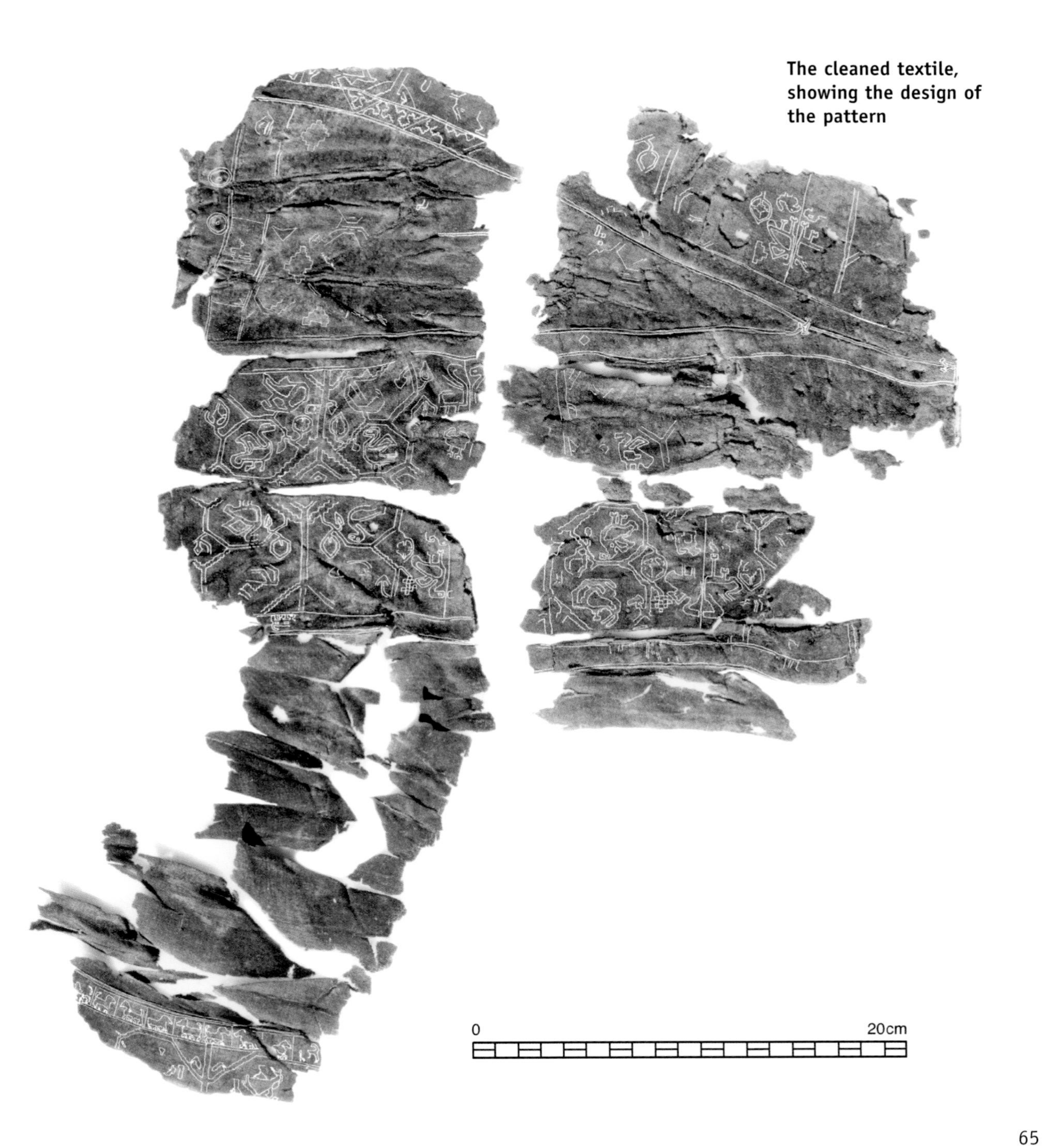

The cleaned textile, showing the design of the pattern

Heather Prosser replicating part of the textile by weaving

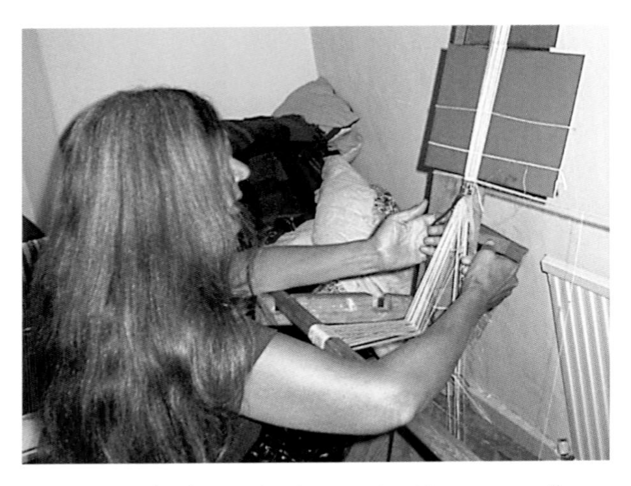

as peeling the layers back one at a time across the folded edge. This edge was creased and folded in on itself in such a way that to fold each layer back would have put the brittle fibres under great stress, causing the fabric to break. A second lightweight fibreglass support was made for the underside of the textile, so that it could easily be reinverted and worked on from both sides.

The fabric had retained no mechanical strength, but proved to be flexible when wet; this made it possible to separate the layers if they were continually supported and not subjected to tension. The layers of textile were separated with a fine spatula while working under a low powered microscope. As each layer was gently lifted, small pieces of flexible film were gradually inserted underneath; once the entire layer had been lifted from one side, the fibreglass support was replaced, the textile turned over and the process repeated. When both sides were free, the entire layer could be lifted free of the body of the textile, the creases across the fold could gently be eased out, and the entire piece laid flat. This process was repeated, replacing the fibreglass supports at intervals with smaller ones, until the centre of the bundle was revealed as the largest decorated piece, folded in on itself.

As the textile was unfolded, it proved to be not one large piece but more than twenty smaller ones that were no longer joined. The bundle of textile had suffered considerable loss of material around two-thirds of its circumference.

Cleaning is an irreversible treatment that can remove important evidence, alter the position of threads and cause details such as stitch holes to be lost; however, it was necessary to remove silt, mud and roots in order to examine the textile in detail. Each piece was laid on gauze stretched over a frame, which was supported across a sink. A trickle of water was directed onto the surface of the textile through a fine tube, and a soft brush was used gently to dislodge the silt; the roots were removed with forceps. The washing was also carried out under a low powered microscope, so that the process could be stopped immediately if any damage to the fibres was observed. Once all the pieces had been cleaned and recorded, they were covered with sheets of Perspex, lightly weighted, and allowed to dry.
The textile air-dried well without shrinkage, although with a brittle, fragile result. Consolidants were considered but very little work has been published on the conservation of charred textile, and trials of PEGs and glycerol gave results that were greasy and obscured the minute detail of the stitching, and so were judged unacceptable.

It is possible that no one will see a complex textile in such detail as the conservator who works on it; a textile that is flexible when wet may not retain this flexibility when dry. It is extremely useful

An image of the lion border, coloured by computer enhancement

if the specialists who are to write the report on the textile are able to visit the laboratory at various times during its conservation, both to see it for themselves and to give advice on observing and recording detail with which the conservator may not be familiar.

Recording

Every stage of the unfolding and conservation was recorded in detail, both photographically and by tracings on transparent film. This careful recording was vital both to locate the many tiny fragments and to relate the main pieces of textile to one another.

Since the textile is both black and permanently creased, and the patterns are extremely small, it is difficult to photograph it in such a way as to show the design. The patterns are now only discernible by the texture of the surface rather than by different colours, and therefore the surface needs to be photographed in a raking light for them to be visible; however, the creasing makes it impossible to light an entire piece of the textile in this way. The patterned parts of the textile were photographed while they were still wet at high magnification. These photographs were then joined together to make large photomontages of each of the patterned pieces, on which the stitches are clearly visible.

The photomontages were used to provide a preliminary outline of the overall design and are being used, in combination with observation of the textile itself, to draw a stitch plan of the design. Fragments of the textile have also been electronically scanned so that magnified images can be enhanced on a computer, and this form of recording, in conjunction with the photographic record, can also be used to produce computer-simulated images with

An embroidered reconstruction of the lion border by Julie Taylor

conjectural colour. This is work in progress, and only some areas have been recorded in this way.

Construction and design

The unfolded textile consists of approximately 780 cm^2 of patterned fabric, and almost twice as much of unpatterned tabby, or plain-woven, linen. The linen textile is very fine, with twenty-five threads per centimetre in both directions, and both the spinning, done by hand using a drop-spindle, and the weaving, on a warp-weighted loom, show an extraordinary degree of skill.

Over about a third of the surviving base fabric, silk and linen threads have been used to decorate the textile with birds and other creatures within a framework of vines, and with borders containing repeating patterns of lions. The textile appears to be part of a garment, perhaps a tunic or dress – it has a hem and a belt loop – but unfortunately too little survives to indicate its detailed shape. Areas of wear suggest that it was not new when lost and we can be confident that its owner was a person of considerable status since the silk that decorates it must have been imported to Britain, while the quality of the needlework suggests that it was produced in a specialist workshop.

To form the patterns, the stitches in the design and the background are worked at right angles to each other, and at intervals both the design and the direction of the stitches reverse. The patterns are worked in paired linen threads, which would have caused it to be slightly raised, and the background filled in with smooth, glossy, single-ply silk stitching.

There are still large gaps in our knowledge. There is no remaining evidence for the colours used, and these have to be guessed at through historical parallels and illustrations. The colours would have made the textile much richer in its appearance, and reconstructions using coloured images can help to bring the textile to life.

Another very important aspect of research into the textile has been the experimental work carried out. The incredibly fine and minute nature of the weave and its degraded state mean that there is still debate as to whether the decoration was embroidered on to the woven surface of the cloth or whether it is a brocading technique, where the decoration is formed by an extra weft on the surface of the tabby ground weave. Both methods would require an enormous degree of skill and both have been replicated.

Although the textile has been described as embroidered, this experimental work has demonstrated that the Llangorse Textile could have been produced either by embroidery or by weaving. Samples were made using both methods, although difficulty in obtaining correct materials meant that neither sample is a truly accurate replica. The embroidered sample appears to be nearest to the original, since it uses a base textile of almost exactly the same thread count and diameter. However, here modern threads were used, for example the background is stitched in two-ply rather than single-ply thread, giving a different visual effect.

The woven sample is not correctly to scale but it is felt that with practice, and with correct materials, an accurate replica could be achieved. Attempts to source correct materials are continuing, as is the drawing of the stitch plan, which is now supplemented by high quality computerised scans. It is hoped that, as this stitch-by-stitch scrutiny of the original fabric continues, further clues will be found that will suggest which technique was used to produce this unique textile.

Louise Mumford

A woven reconstruction of the lion border on the Llangorse textile

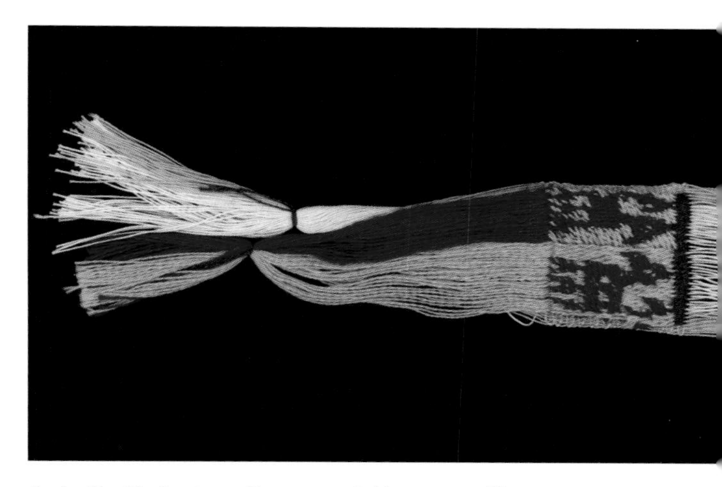

BROOKES, M., LISTER, A., EASTOP, D. & BENNET, T. 1996. Artifact or Information? Articulating the Conflicts, 16-21. In . ROY, A. & SMITH, P. (eds). *Conserving Archaeological Textiles. Archaeological Conservation and its Consequences*. IIC Conference, Copenhagen

GRANGER-TAYLOR, H. & PRITCHARD, F. 2002. A Fine Quality 'Insular' embroidery from the Late Ninth/ Early Tenth Century Crannog at Llangorse, Near Brecon, 90-99. In REDKNAP, M. (ed.). *Pattern and Purpose in Insular Art: Pre-prints of the Fourth International Conference on Insular Art*, Oxbow Books, Oxford.

MUMFORD, C. L. 2002. The Conservation of the Llangorse Textile, 471-483. In HOFFMANN, P., SPRIGGS, J. A., GRANT, T., COOK C. & RECHT A. (eds) Proceedings of the 8th ICOM Group on Wet Organic Archaeological Materials Conference, Stockholm 2001.

REDKNAP, M. & LANE, A. 1994. The Early Medieval Crannog at Llangorse, Powys: an Interim Statement of the 1989-1993 Seasons. *International Journal of Nautical Archaeology*, 23, 189-205.

MUMFORD, L. & REDKNAP, M. 1998. Worn by a Welsh Queen? *Amgueddfa: Yearbook of the National Museums & Galleries of Wales 1998-9*, 52-54.

Examination

Arguably the most important single aspect of museum curatorship is examination. There is a long and respectable history whereby works of art and history were inspected and assessed to determine their nature, origins, style etc. This can be called connoisseurship and relies on the knowledge and experience of academics and craftsmen to recognise parallels with objects and materials of known provenance. Museums have traditionally been the repositories of collections whose origins are known and whose status and authenticity is certain. They are our touchstones of integrity with which the doubtful, the copy and the possible fake are compared. Unfortunately, life is not that simple and all museums have objects in them for which authenticity cannot be guaranteed and connoisseurship does not provide an unequivocal answer. Increasingly the technical and scientific examination of historic, artistic and natural science material is providing us with objective information. However, the information on its own is useless unless correctly interpreted – which takes us back to the experienced and knowledgeable curator.

The aim of most current examination techniques is to elicit as much information as possible from an object without affecting it in any way, and to use the information to correctly interpret the object, assess its condition and therefore be able to conserve it sympathetically. This is becoming increasingly possible with the expanding use of sophisticated analytical equipment within museums.

Most examination techniques are based on vision. Careful inspection in good lighting conditions will tell us perhaps as much as we need to know. Enhancing vision with the use of microscopes allows the examination of microscopic areas to show vital details. Using different energies from light – ultra violet and infra red – will highlight different aspect of pigments, varnishes, old restoration etc. X-rays allow us to see beneath the surface and note the internal structure of materials – perhaps the iron artefact in a block of archaeological corrosion product, or a previous painting under a present one.

Irradiating an object with different energies causes them to be absorbed or reflected, depending on what substance they are hitting. The absorbed and reflected energies can then be analysed to give an identification of that substance. The recent Treasure Act, which covers material found in the ground that may be of precious metal, means that the objects are analysed by a Scanning Electron Microscope with Energy Dispersive X-Rays to determine the presence and amount of silver and gold in the material.

Examination and the analytical techniques that go with it provide answers to particular questions. However, the interpretation of the answer is all important. The identification of gold on an analysed spot on a coin does not necessarily mean the coin is a gold one. The analyst may just 'coincidentally' pick up the only fragment of gold on the coin and it may have come from an adjacent object in the surrounding soil or whatever. The identification of a later pigment on a supposedly early painting does not damn it necessarily as a fake. However, good examination techniques involving our cultural heritage have advanced our knowledge immensely – and continue to do so.

Leaves of iron
An unusual Victorian ledger

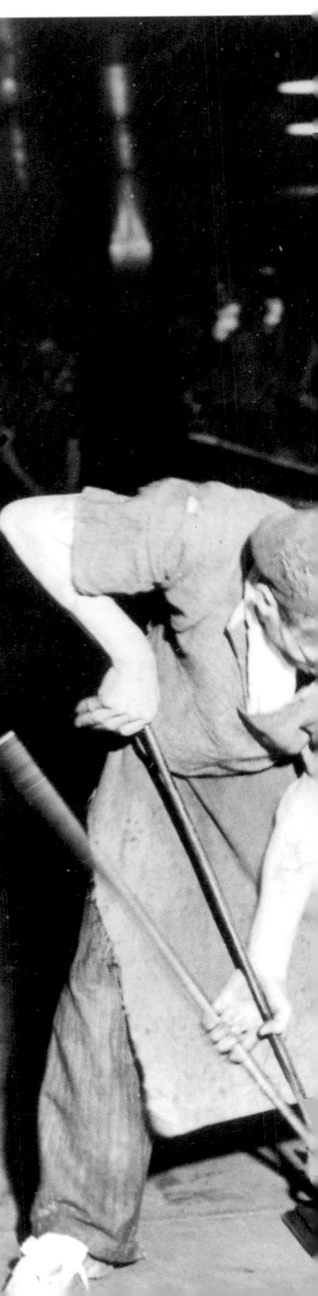

Iron being rolled into sheets. The sheets were so thin that it would have been impossible to manipulate the hot iron without it bending unless it was rolled as a number of sheets together. This also conserved heat – single sheets would have lost heat too quickly to enable rolling to take place. The iron was therefore repeatedly 'doubled' as it lengthened during rolling

Industrial objects can present different problems from those encountered by the more established museum conservation disciplines. During the industrial revolution many new materials were being manufactured and used to build increasingly complex items, the long-term survival of which was not a consideration. Industrial museums in the past traditionally relied on engineers to restore objects and keep the collections in good order, for instance by replacing parts on working machinery. However, some small and non-functional objects were neglected. The situation has now changed considerably but, as with many social and industrial history collections, there are many problematic materials and composite objects posing difficult problems in terms of their long-term stability.

The Melingriffith specimen book is a rare and unusual leather-bound, ledger-style book containing a collection of thinly rolled iron sheets, which gives a unique glimpse into the industrial production of iron in Wales during the latter part of the nineteenth century. This book was commissioned and partly manufactured by Thomas W. Booker & Co at their Melingriffith tinplate works in Cardiff in the late 1860s and early 1870s. The book consists of seventy-nine (originally eighty) very thin, untinned iron sheets; these were adhered into textile guards and then sewn through the folds into a binding.

A page from the template book before conservation

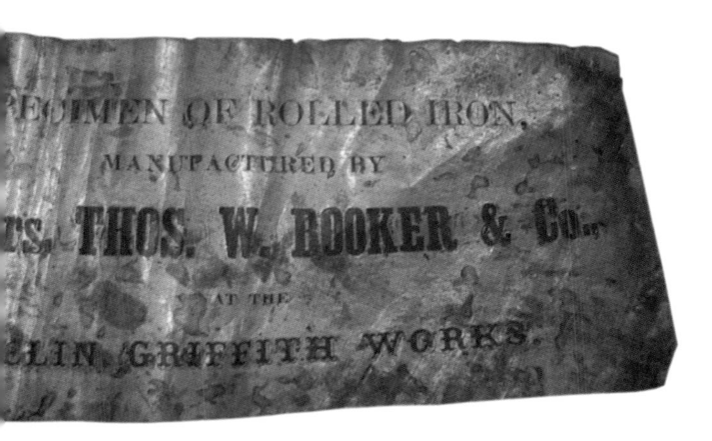

Each 'page' of sheet iron was printed with the legend:
SPECIMEN OF ROLLED IRON, MANUFACTURED BY MESSERS. THOMAS W. BOOKER & CO., AT THE MELIN GRIFFITH WORKS.

The specimen sheets are too thin for any industrial use, but instead aimed to display the skill of the manufacturers: precision was demonstrated both by the thinness of the sheets, (approximately 50 microns thick; modern paper is approx 30 microns thick), and by a consistency in quality throughout the volume.

The book would have acted as an advertisement, perhaps sitting on the director's table for potential clients to look through. Such specimens seem to have been common at the period of their manufacture, but this type of object has seldom been kept, let alone survived its storage environment. The fact that even single specimen sheets are now rare shows the unique historical value of this book.

As with many small objects held in industrial collections, the specimen book had not been stored in any stipulated conditions and had never undergone conservation treatment in the past. When it was selected to undergo a programme of treatment to prepare it for future display, the book needed material and structural stabilisation. To achieve this it was necessary for it to be assessed and treated by different material specialists, including a book conservator, a paper conservator and an objects conservator.

Sheet iron was manufactured from cast or scrap iron by puddling, and then rolling the metal into bars. These bars were then put through cycles of heating, rolling, folding and annealing to flatten them into sheets that could be cut to size, coated in molten tin and used in the burgeoning canning and oil industries. The sheets produced for this book could be characterised as a thick foil; they were flexible and easily folded, with a consistent thickness throughout the volume. The pages measured approximately 170 x 330 mm. They were not tinned, the iron surface was instead protected by an organic coating. Solubility tests, FTIR examination and interpretation of historical data suggest that the coating consisted of a mixture of materials, probably including a type of wax for flexibility and a resin for strength. However, the exact nature of these constituents could not be pinpointed. The coating was applied as a finish; heat was used to reemulsify a wax-based layer, causing all excess material to run off leaving a very thin, even coating.

Printing inks of the time typically consisted of linseed oil with carbon black pigment. Microscopic analysis showed that the ink had been printed as if the metal were paper, on top of the wax/resin coating, as this not only gave primary protection to the whole of the metal surface but also provided

a more receptive surface for the ink.
The sample book was bound in a high quality, bespoke stationery binding, affording both the strength and feel of a ledger. The book had a full covering of rolled and dyed calfskin, decorated with gold-tooled (impressed gilding) beading and written legends. Inside the leather binding, blue and marbled paper made up the protective endpapers at the front and back of the book.

Condition and conservation

The treatment of this object was complex due to the range of materials used in its manufacture. Widely differing materials in close proximity in an object can affect the decay environment as actively as external factors, even speeding up or exaggerating decay phenomena. For example, whilst contact with the iron had stained the paper of the specimen book, the iron itself was also in danger of further corrosion by the acid breakdown products of the paper and leather. A major issue when treating composite objects is therefore to slow down or prevent these interactions, while not compromising the integrity of the object as a whole.

Although the desired result of this conservation project was to display the book as a whole, it was impossible to treat it without taking it apart. This was done mechanically using a scalpel and steel spatula, which revealed the binding structure and left the book in two parts: the sewn block of metal pages, and the leather and paper covers and spine. Once separate, the specimen block was stored in a sealed polythene bag with silica gel to halt any active corrosion of the metal pages, and the binding structure was kept at an ambient relative humidity to prevent desiccation and further damage to the organic components of the book.

The metal pages were heavily affected by physical wear such as tearing and folding as well as some chemical decay. Most of the sheets were disfigured by corrosion and the degradation of the organic coating. Surface damage, including pinhole corrosion, was present in places. The condition of the sheets necessitated interventive conservation work, including localised mechanical cleaning while retaining as much of the organic coating as possible.

First, creases were stroked out of the pages, and folded tears or corners were lifted and smoothed carefully back into position. Areas of the coating that had pooled over time were removed with a scalpel, although those covering the ink inscription were found to take the ink away with them, and so were cleaned flush with the lettering and left in place. Flash rusting was removed with a glass bristle brush. Red brittle corrosion patches and sweaty fingerprint patches were treated in the same way, to reduce them in size and thickness without exposing bare metal. Swabs of IMS were then used to degrease the fingerprints, and the fore edges of each page, as these were especially dirty and greasy. This treatment lightened the sheets and gave them a more homogeneous sheen, but care was taken not to expose the shiny metal surface, or touch areas of lettering or 'clean' coating. Finally, layers of black surface dust were removed from all un-inked areas of the page with dry swabs.

The leather and paper covers and spine were in a very weak state. The leather especially had suffered both through use and while in storage. There was a high degree of abrasive wear, and dark patches of water damage alongside dry cracking and embrittlement. Red rot was also occurring in places, visible as the disintegration of the leather into a red powder. The joints and corners of the cover were in

The book during conservation of metal pages

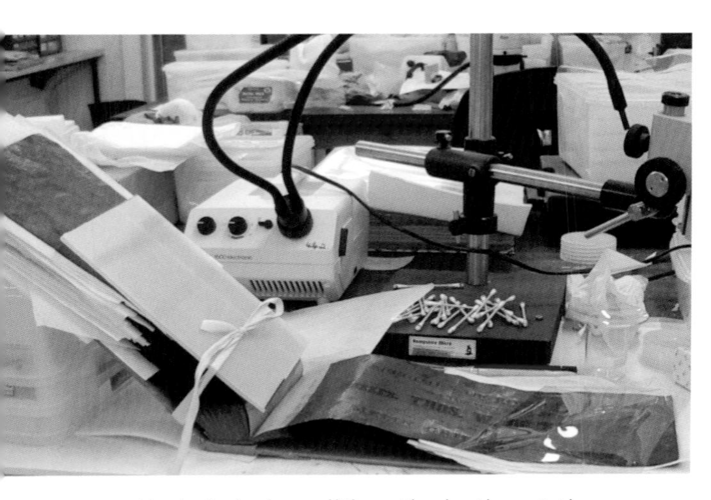

particularly bad condition: the leather at these points of stress was fragile, often powdery, and beginning to tear apart.

As the sewing and internal hard boards were intact and strong, conservation of the binding focused on rebuilding the leather joints. The key to this part of the treatment was to enable the book to be opened and closed without damage to the binding or its contents. The internal elements of the binding were therefore taken apart as far as possible to allow any weakened components, such as the spine linings, to be strengthened by backing with Japanese tissue and wheat starch paste. The four corners of the boards were repaired with specially prepared pieces of new leather; these were moulded over the corners and tucked under the remaining original leather. A further new piece was also adhered tightly over the spine and under the original leather, to create new joints. Finally, in order to counter damage already done by red rot and wear, the whole of the leather cover was consolidated with an inert artificial polymer (Klucel G™)

The cloth guards and endpapers were stained by corrosion from the specimen sheets. These stains can cause and accelerate the acidic decay of organic materials. However, removal of the pages from their textile guards was considered unacceptable due to the physical stress this would cause; therefore conservation of the guards had to be limited to brushing away dirt as each metal page was cleaned.

Paper often discolours and becomes brittle with age. Although the paper used in this binding was in remarkably good condition, there was surface staining from contact with the leather, and the flyleaves were faded and brittle along their exposed fore edges. The blue paper was also covered in rust stains and tiny iron concretions, which were both disfiguring and a chemical threat to the fibres. Full detachment of the end papers was again felt to be unacceptable and so wet treatments were restricted, especially as there were the additional risks of delamination of the flyleaves, and leaching of pigments. As such, procedures such as chemical removal of the iron staining and buffering had to be improvised for localised and controlled treatment.

The papers were first cleaned using grated eraser granules, rubbed over the surface with cotton wool. This removed a degree of dirt, and brightened the blue paper slightly. However, it also removed some of the pigments from the marbled papers, so it could not be used on these. The blue paper was then cleaned, using tap water swabbed onto the surface and then immediately drawn out with blotting paper and a hot spatula. This treatment served to rehydrate and realign the paper fibres, but had limited visible impact.

Tests showed that the iron staining on the paper could not be removed safely using chemicals, so treatment was restricted to mechanical removal of the concretions, using a scalpel under the microscope. This reduced both the visual disfigurement and the chemical risk to the paper surface. In order to combat residual acidity within the paper, a buffering solution of magnesium bicarbonate was swabbed across the blue side of the endpapers in a series of applications. The fore edges of the flyleaf papers were further strengthened and repaired using tinted Japanese tissue.

Anoxic storage and display

The conflicting environmental conditions required for the various materials in the book posed problems for its storage. Many factors needed consideration, for example ultraviolet radiation, visible light and temperature, but the main problem was deciding the optimum level of relative humidity.

Organic materials exist in equilibrium with their environment, swelling and shrinking as their water content changes in line with that of the surrounding air. Too dry conditions therefore can result in irreversible fibre shrinkage and brittleness, as seen by the damage to the Melingriffith leather cover, while damp leads to staining, excessive swelling and possible biological attack. Variable relative humidities can also cause stress, such as cracking and loss of strength if the cycle is too fast for the material to react uniformly. Therefore, a stable, mid-range humidity of 45-60 per cent is the most desirable for these materials.

In contrast, inorganic materials do not react to the environment in the same way, and with reactive metals such as iron, desiccation is the main option used within museum environments for inhibiting electrochemical corrosion, and to keep salts below their deliquescence points. Historical metals are generally more robust than archaeological ones, and can often be safely stored at a stable mid-range humidity alongside organics. However, the Melingriffith specimen sheets displayed active corrosion and so were already vulnerable; this, in conjunction with the book's historical importance, meant that a solution had to be found for storing and displaying the object in a more suitable environment for both the organic and inorganic components.

Cleaned and uncleaned pages of the book

A mid-range humidity would be the normal choice for such an object, but then action would have to be taken to protect the pages. For example, to prevent the continued deterioration of pitted and corroded regions, the original coating could be removed or these areas could be covered with a modern coating, such as microcrystalline wax, but this option would be very invasive, and irreversible. Desiccation would be ideal for the metal pages but would cause considerable damage to the organic components of the object. The option of separation and separate environmental storage of the main binding and specimen block was considered, however

Creased and damaged pages, and corrosion at the edge of the pages

this would still leave the cloth guards and organic coating in danger of embrittlement. If the only option for safe preservation was separation, then displaying the book complete seemed contradictory to its best interests.

An anoxic environment offers a solution to many of these problems, as it eliminates one agent vital to the decay of both organic and inorganic materials. Without oxygen, corrosion of the metal sheets is suppressed and so a mid-range humidity can be maintained for the safe storage of the organic components. In addition, the coating can remain in place without the risk of further damage to the iron surface.

The technology to produce such an environment to museum standards has become much more widespread in the last few years. Nitrogen can be used as the exclusion agent, and cases can now be sealed hermetically. Anoxic storage can also now be achieved relatively cheaply and efficiently for smaller objects with the use of barrier films. These are multi-layered laminates that include a gas and water vapour barrier film and a heat sealable layer. They can be made into envelopes, with seams that are effective over a matter of years. Oxygen scavengers inserted into the system chemically dispose of all the available oxygen, and so a suitable microclimate is created.

Oxygen scavengers are now widely available. Some have a built-in desiccant that takes the relative humidity to below 5 per cent, while others are 'moisture neutral', and therefore more appropriate for use with organic or composite materials such as the Melingriffith specimen book.

An anoxic microclimate was constructed for the book using barrier film and oxygen scavengers. Additional precautions were taken to reduce the possibility of adverse reactions occurring from such mixed materials remaining in direct contact with each other. A divider was used to separate the leather from the paper, the paper from the iron, and each iron sheet from the next, in order to halt the transfer of decay products. An acid-free paper, incorporating activated charcoal, was used to separate the leather and paper layers, and polyester film used to separate each metal specimen sheet from the next. Bindings are structurally most stable

The open book, showing the cloth guards and end papers before conservation

when closed and stored flat, and for this reason the book was sealed into the gas-barrier envelope in this way, with the entire package stored in an archival storage box. For exhibition purposes it is envisaged that a sealed anoxic case will be constructed to give the book similar environmental protection while on display.

Felicity Woor and Walter Gneisinger

Top: The bookbinding, during conversation
Below: The template book, after conservation

CHAPPELL, E. L. 1995. *Historic Melingriffith: An Account of Pentyrch Iron Works and Melingriffith Tinplate Works*. Merton Priory Press, Cardiff. (2nd Edition)

MARKS, P. J. M. 1998. *The British Library Guide to Bookbinding, History and Techniques*. University of Toronto Press Inc., Toronto.

MINCHINGTON, W. E. 1957. *The British Tinplate Industry: A History*. Clarendon Press, Oxford.

Treasure Trove and the Treasure Act 1996

The ancient common law of Treasure Trove dates back to the twelfth century. When objects made of gold or silver were discovered in the ground they became the subject of a coroner's inquest to decide whether they were buried 'with the intention of being recovered', as opposed to being lost, abandoned or deposited in the ground as a ritual offering. If the treasure was declared to have been lost or ritually deposited, it became the property of the landowner. If, however, the coroner's jury decided that the treasure was hidden for safe keeping with the intention of recovery, and with no known heirs, it was declared to be Treasure Trove and then belonged to the crown. In more recent times, such treasure was offered to an appropriate local or national museum, which 'rewarded' the finder with the commercial value of the objects.

The law of Treasure Trove was superseded by the Treasure Act 1996 in England, Wales and Northern Ireland. This was intended to clarify the laws for many of those involved in the process – from finders and landowners to archaeologists and coroners. There were so many ambivalent areas in the old Treasure Trove laws: were items buried with a view to recovery? Was a hoard of gold and silver torcs deposited for safe keeping or for ritual deposition? Was it right that in a hoard containing a variety of materials, only the gold and silver were considered treasure? What indeed was meant by 'gold' or 'silver'?

The new Act defines treasure slightly differently, and removes the need to establish that objects were hidden with the intention of recovery. Objects other than coins should contain at least 10 per cent gold or silver by weight, and be at least 300 years old when found. Any object, of whatever composition, found in association with such an object is also deemed Treasure.

Where at least two coins of 10 per cent gold or silver and at least 300 years old are found together, these are Treasure; when coins are made from less than 10 per cent precious metal there must be at least ten to qualify as Treasure. The objects still need to go before a coroner, and if deemed Treasure will be offered to an appropriate museum to purchase at their market value – as determined by an independent valuation committee.

In 2002, the Treasure Act was amended to include prehistoric 'base' metal hoards as Treasure, that is pre-Roman metal work that does not contain 10 per cent gold or silver, but where at least two such metal objects have been buried together. A prehistoric single find, other than a coin, is also Treasure if any part of it is made of precious metal.

The Treasure Act 1996 Code of Practice (Revised). 2002. Department for Culture, Media and Sport

The Rogiet hoard of late 3rd-century silvered base metal coins found in 1998, classified as Treasure under the 1996 Treasure Act

How the leopard got its spots
A Roman cup in Wales

The leopard cup, as first reported

In November 2002, a metal detectorist was prospecting on farm land near Abergavenny when he got a weak signal towards one edge of the field. After digging to a depth of about sixty-five centimetres, he found an upturned bronze vessel; while examining the bottom of the small pit he had excavated, he discovered a crouching animal that had formed the handle of the vessel.

The detectorist reported the find through the Portable Antiquities Scheme, which made it possible for archaeologists to carry out a field evaluation. The find spot was assessed and this in turn shed light on the archaeological context of the cup. It seems likely that the bronze cup, with its zoomorphic leopard handle, accompanied a cremation burial that formed part of a cemetery lying beside a Roman road some distance from the fort at Abergavenny. There is a growing amount of evidence for a civilian settlement dating from the second to fourth centuries in the vicinity of the cremation cemetery. Cremations dating from the first to the third centuries have been found on a number of Roman settlements – both military and civilian – and occasionally in rural locations in Wales. They range from simple pockets of ash and bone in pits to more formal burials in containers, sometimes accompanied by grave goods (Arnold & Davies 2000). The cup was found upside down; it does not appear to have been used as the vessel or urn in which the remains of the dead were deposited, but rather as an associated grave item.

The cup is manufactured from leaded bronze, and has a fine green patinated surface. It is approximately ten centimetres high with the leopard handle placed on the vessel so that it peers over the rim. The leopard was originally attached to the cup using a tin lead solder, with its front feet resting on the rim, while its rear feet were attached to the belly of the cup. The face is extremely finely delineated, with carefully cast canine teeth, incised lines for its whiskers, and inlaid eyes. The animal is presumed to be a leopard because its body has been decorated with a large number of silver spots. In Roman mythology the leopard or panther appears as the companion of Bacchus, and is also depicted pulling his chariot. Bacchus was the god of wine, whose worship involved feasting, drinking, music and dancing, so the choice of a leopard for the handle of what might have been a wine cup would have been

A depiction of Bacchus and a leopard on the Mildenhall 'Great Dish' © British Museum

very appropriate. Leopards captured in Africa were also popular with the Romans for display and fighting in the amphitheatre (Toynbee 1973).

The leopard cup would undoubtedly have been a costly imported item. Roman cups with zoomorphic handles have been found from a variety of sites and span a wide range of dates (Curle 1923). This includes, for example, the tigress handle from the fifth-century Roman Hoxne hoard in Suffolk (Bland & Johns 1993). However, the closest British parallel is from the Traprain Law treasure, discovered in Scotland during excavations in 1919. This treasure consists of over a hundred objects, predominantly made of silver and unceremoniously dumped together as scrap. Amongst this were two silver 'panther handles', which originally would have been attached to the rim of a vessel by their front feet and soldered to the body of the vessel by their hind feet – as with the Abergavennny cup. One of the handles is, in fact, a leopard, with decorative spots punched onto its body. Although the Traprain Law hoard is dated to about AD 400 by association with coins of Honorius (AD 395-423), it is likely that some of the treasure was manufactured at an earlier date (Curle 1923). The shape and form of the Abergavenny cup are close to those dating from the first century AD. Similar cups have been found, for example, at Pompeii. The context of the Abergavenny cup find within a cremation rather than an inhumation burial also tends to suggest an earlier date of manufacture.

The leopard and the cup arrived at the Museum detached, just as they had been discovered. Some of the more superficial mud had been carefully cleaned away by a conservator to enable initial recording before it reached the Museum, but areas of concreted corrosion remained on much of the surface. Both the cup and the leopard underwent a series of thorough examinations before any interventive conservation was undertaken.

Initial examination took the form of detailed observations of the surface under a low powered microscope. The cup and the leopard had both survived remarkably intact. The colour of the two components varied; they were both made from leaded bronze, but the surface of the leopard was much greyer in appearance than that of the cup. On both the cup and the leopard it was possible to see the preservation of the dendritic structure of the metal,

confirming that both components of the object had been cast.

The leopard handle was made separately and is an exceptional example of 'lost wax' casting. Much of the original incised and cast detail has remained preserved within the surface corrosion products, including finely delineated features on the paws, ears and face. The leopard is also extremely naturalistic, even showing the animal's musculature on the underside, which is not easily visible when the handle is attached to the cup.

There was some visible damage to several extremities of the leopard itself: one hind leg was missing part of its surface, the ends of the ears were chipped and there was also damage to the tail, one of the paws and one eyebrow. However, considering the extent to which the metal had corroded, the surviving patinated surface of the handle was in excellent condition. The leopard had fifty-seven silver spots, of which twenty-eight still contained the inlaid metal.

The voids for the spots appear to have been chiselled out from the cast body of the leopard, and many were slightly undercut sideways into the body to help prevent the inlaid silver from dropping out. They varied considerably in shape from spherical to tapering lozenges and often appeared relatively crudely made compared to the finely executed cast of the leopard's body. Some of the empty spots were not visible before conservation, as concretions had built up over the cavities obscuring them from view.

On the leopard's back just above the tail are several irregular holes in the surface, the results of casting flaws. Although these are not particularly noticeable, there is a large group of carved spots here, probably deliberately placed to help obscure some of the fault.

The underside of the tail and the fine canine teeth appear to have been carved away further after casting. There are ridges, like knife cuts, running across the tail and some areas appear faceted as though it was pared down along its length. The tail and canine teeth were probably originally cast more thickly, but cut away to form such fine features after casting.

The cup was cast in a mould from leaded bronze and then turned on a lathe with a sharp tool held against the metal to remove any irregularities from the surface and to produce an impressively symmetrical finished and polished form. A sharp tool would also have been used with the lathe to form the deep concentric circles visible on the base of the vessel.

The very fine patina on the cup was disrupted by concretions on the surface. This was especially apparent in areas where remains of solder had corroded and were visible as a U-shaped area on the side where the leopard had been attached to the vessel. Remnants of white metal were present on the rim in two places where the front paws were once attached – but there was no evidence of anything similar on the opposite side of the rim. This confirmed that the vessel had only ever had one handle, and not a pair. There were also a number of old scratches and dents especially at the bottom of the cup. Three small areas of solder visible on the foot of the vessel might well have been attached to spikes used to hold the cup securely as it was turned on the lathe (Brown 1976).

X-rays were taken to help clarify some of the initial observations. The leopard handle was manufactured from such heavily leaded bronze that only the extremities of the animal revealed any useful detail. It could be seen that there was a break through the leopard's tail, though it remained attached and in place, as its tip was fixed to the

An X-ray of the vessel, showing turning rings

foot area. The X-ray also showed some of the filling in the spots as small separate metal areas.

Several X-rays of the cup produced good images; the walls of the vessel were thinner than the leopard, and the metal was less heavily leaded. The X-rays confirmed it had been turned all over; bands can be seen across the cup, and the holding mark where the vessel was held fast whilst it was turned is visible in the centre of the base. The areas where solder attached the rear feet of the leopard to the cup are also clearly visible as the solder is denser than the bronze.

Cleaning

The leopard and cup were cleaned primarily by removing soil and corrosion products under a low-powered microscope, using combinations of a scalpel, toothpick, IMS swabs and a fine paint brush. As the cleaning progressed, more spots became visible under the incrustations; most were hollow and contained no infill, but were capped by a thin layer of hard corrosion, which was black on the underside. These 'caps' were kept for analysis. Some of the empty spots still contained soil – which when brushed away left a black, grey or brown material overlying the bronze. This was initially left in situ to verify by analysis what material had once filled the spot.

The under-surface of the feet had been roughened to help solder the leopard to the cup. The tips of the ears, the tail, and one paw had lost their smooth outer surface, exposing a layer of powdery green corrosion over a very thin mineralised core. The corrosion crust was so thick that no metal was visible even in damaged areas. Adjacent to these damaged areas, a fine crazing had occurred on the surface patination and it was necessary to consolidate these regions to prevent any further loss of the surface.

Slow and careful cleaning was necessary when removing surface dirt so as not to damage the underlying patina, especially from the front paws and between the teeth. During preliminary SEM analysis (see p.92) it could also be seen that one of the canine teeth was cracked through and was being held in place only by the surrounding soil and

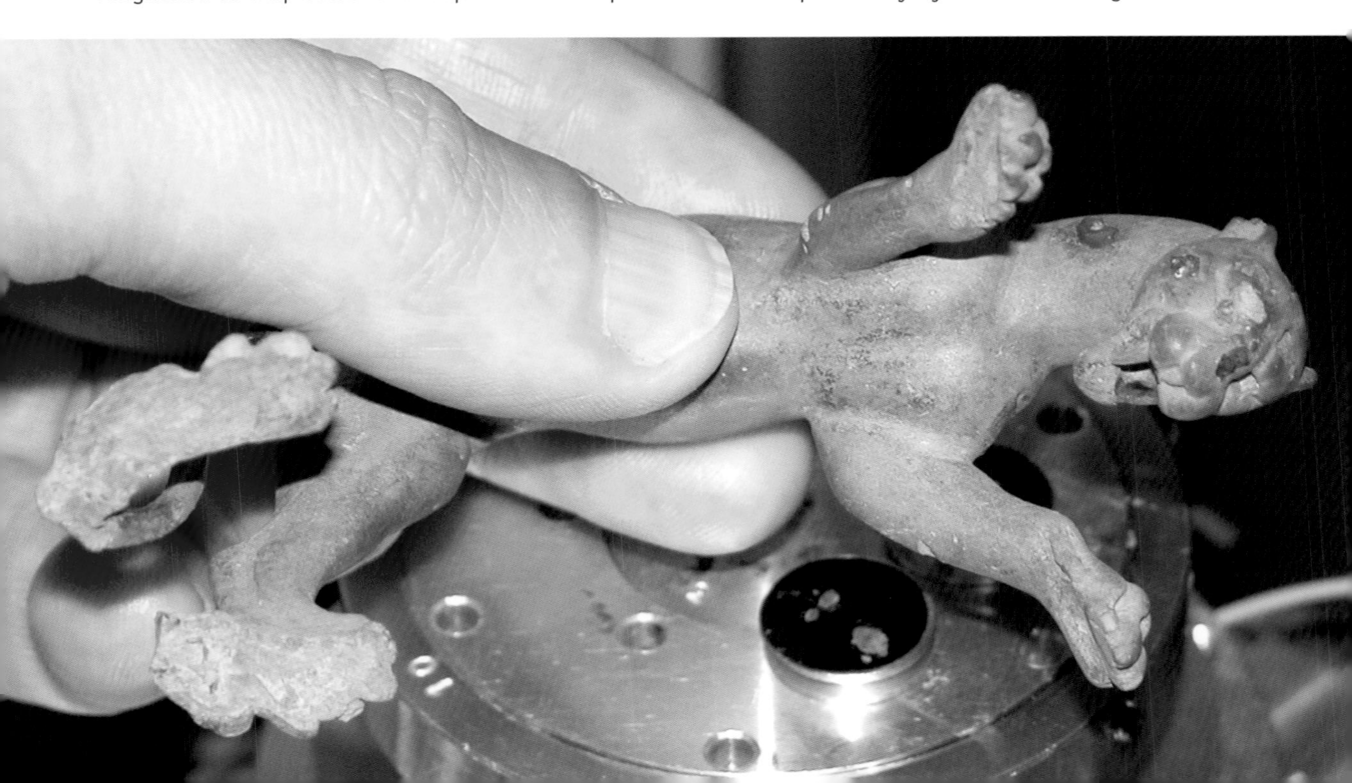

The leopard being put in the SEM chamber

corrosion products. This was consolidated (with dilute Paraloid B-72™) so as to avoid any danger of displacement and loss when soil was removed from the mouth. Following cleaning, finely cast facial details could be seen; whiskers were suggested by finely incised lines on the face.

When cleaning dirt from around the eyes, one of them became detached. The eye is approximately 1 mm in diameter, and its socket contained loose dirt but no traces of any material that might originally have been used to hold the eye in place. When the dirt was brushed away, a small cleanly made square socket was left, which was originally cast rather than cut into the bronze. The eye itself was kept safe until it could be put back at the end of the conservation process.

The silver spots on the leopard were cleaned using cotton wool and calcium carbonate swabs; this acted as a very mild abrasive and allowed the majority of the black surface corrosion to be removed without scratching the relatively soft and vulnerable underlying silver. These areas were then rinsed locally with IMS.

The body of the cup was mostly in good condition and had a very fine patination. Some of the surface had slight pitting and other areas were slightly brighter green and not so smooth. The area around the middle of the cup was much more heavily covered in soil and concretions than the other areas. A scalpel was used to remove incrustations from the surface of the cup; turned lines at the rim and the base needed further cleaning with a sharpened toothpick, and the whole surface was regularly swabbed with IMS to remove soil and loose corrosion products.

A Scanning Electron Micrograph of the leopard's mouth, showing the cracked canine teeth held in place by mud, and the preserved dendrictic structure of the metal

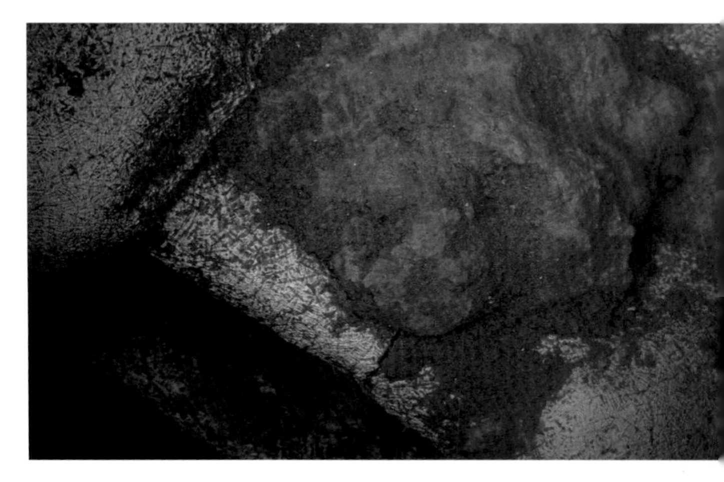

Chemical analysis

The chemical composition of the cup, the leopard, its eyes and its spots were examined by SEM EDX. This enabled us to confirm that the main alloy used for both the leopard handle and the cup was leaded bronze, which is principally made of copper and tin with lead added to improve the quality of the cast (it lowers the melting point of the alloy and makes the metal flow more easily). This SEM EDX analysis did not require destructive sampling, as both the cup and the leopard fitted inside the specimen chamber. However, the effects of corrosion and the presence of contaminants from the soil such as aluminium and silicon meant that results from these surface analyses did not provide a true representation of the original composition of the metal. If it proves necessary in the future to establish exact quantities of all the elements present, for example to determine the source of the metal, uncontaminated samples will have to be drilled from below the corrosion layers. The pattern of metallic dendritic structures from the casting was very visible under the high magnification

of the SEM, as were multiple cracks occurring throughout the surface corrosion.

The spots on the leopard were found to consist of relatively pure silver (95-98 per cent). Areas of concretions that had formed small caps overlying empty holes were also predominantly silver, while the bases of the holes themselves also showed traces of silver in the bronze. This suggests that all the spots were made of the same metal.

Phosphorus was present on all the surfaces analysed, and its occurrence at such high levels may have come from the bone in a cremation or burial. The object was found well below the plough soil in a field laid to pasture for many years, and so it is improbable that such high levels of phosphates came from agricultural fertilisers. This information supports the proposal that the find was part of a funerary deposit.

The eyes are yellowish brown and about 1 mm across, with slight indentations in the middle. A combination of FTIR and SEM EDX analysis was used to identify the material. The analyses were complicated, as dirt and soil are difficult to remove from the surface of very small, rough and degraded substances without sampling; therefore elements such as iron from the soil and phosphorus from the burial showed up in the results as contaminants. The material from which the eye was made had also degraded, making the composition of the original substance difficult to interpret. The FTIR was used to analyse organic molecules present in the eye, and the outcome here indicated a resinous material had been used.

The SEM is more often used to analyse inorganic elements, but a high carbon level was detected in the eye, which indicated a high organic content. Sulphur was also present, and this occurs in Baltic amber; under high magnification there was a hexagonal pattern to the structure, also indicative of amber (Shashoua 2002).

Although the analytical results were not conclusive, given the care with which the leopard had been manufactured it seems likely that a material of some value would have been used. Amber, which fitted to some extent with both the FTIR and the SEM results, was a prized material in the Early Roman Empire and a trade route had been established from the Baltic to Rome. Pliny the Elder, (First century AD), writes of amber as both a fashionable and expensive commodity, claiming that 'Its rating among luxuries is so high that a human figurine, however small, is more expensive than a number of human

A detail of the leopard's face, showing the inlaid eye and incised details

beings, alive and in good health'. Both in terms of colour and value, amber seems an appropriate material for the eyes of such a fine feline.

Finishing

When cleaning and analyses were complete, the cup was coated with a lacquer to protect the surface, and this also contained a copper corrosion inhibitor to help stabilise the underlying metal. Two thin coats were applied using a brush, and innumerable cracks and fissures were temporarily revealed as the solution penetrated the corrosion layers. It is hoped that this coating will strengthen and consolidate the surface, preventing any further loss of detail.

Two further steps were then carried out to complete the conservation work. The eye socket was filled with an acrylic adhesive mixed with glass micro-balloons and powdered pigments, and the eye was returned to the correct position on the leopard's face. Finally, the cup and leopard were put back together. It was relatively easy to tell exactly where the leopard was joined to the cup because of the remains of solder marks where the feet had rested. The object had been so carefully crafted that the leopard balanced in its correct position on the side of the cup, and was easily glued into place.

The trouble taken to manufacture such a beautifully crafted object outweighs the fact that it is made largely from base metal. It is a work of great precision; in fact, such an accurate and naturalistic model suggests the leopard handle was produced by someone who had first-hand knowledge of big cats. The object is mostly bronze, the amber eyes are minute, and it is possible that the silver spots were an afterthought. The recesses for the spots had been cut into the body after completion and not cast in as the eye sockets were; the silver was also inlaid and smoothed over in a relatively coarse fashion compared to the care taken over the original cast. This raises the question of whether the handle had originally been a panther, embellished at a later date.

The leopard cup has now been acquired for the national collections. Its chance survival in such good condition adds to its value as a unique museum piece. The corrosion is thick, riddled with fissures and very delicate; some of the surface has already gone. Disturbance of the object's relatively stable microenvironment within the soil for any length of time, for example by deep ploughing, would almost certainly have resulted in the loss of far more of the surface patina, and therein much of the form and detail of the leopard. The metal detectorist who discovered the object had the foresight not to try to clean the cup at all, but to report the find promptly while it was still covered in mud. This enabled conservation treatment to be undertaken to

The whole cup, after conservation work was completed

ensure its long-term preservation, as well as maximising the potential for research on the cup.

Mary Davis

ARNOLD, C. J. & DAVIES, J. L. 2000. *Roman and Early Medieval Wales*. Sutton Publishing, Stroud.

BLAND, R. & JOHNS, C. 1993. *The Hoxne Treasure: an illustrated introduction*. British Museum Press, London.

BROWN, D. 1976. Bronze and Pewter, 25-42. In STRONG, D. & BROWN, D. (eds). *Roman Crafts*. Duckworth, London.

CURLE, A. O. 1923. *The Treasure of Traprain: A Scottish hoard of Roman silver plate*. Maclehose, Jackson and Co. Glasgow.

PLINY *Natural History*, Book XXXVII. Loeb Classical Library, Harvard 2001.

SHASHOUA, Y. 2002. Degradation and inhibitive conservation of Baltic amber in museum collections. www.natmus.dk/cons/reports/2002/amber/amber.pdf

TOYNBEE, J. M. C. 1973. *Animals in Roman Life and Art*. Thames and Hudson, London.

The Portable Antiquities Scheme and Finds Liaison Officers

At the same time as the new Treasure Act was introduced, the Portable Antiquities Scheme was set up by the government to encourage the reporting of artefacts that do not fall under the definition of Treasure. Recording the accurate provenance and typology of objects that are not Treasure provides an enormous amount of information to archaeologists. Many objects, especially those found by metal detectorists, were not being seen or recorded, and this distorted an already skewed picture of the material culture of many regions. This scheme, unlike the reporting of Treasure, is entirely voluntary: finders can report their objects to Finds Liaison Officers who are based in regional centres throughout the country. Where possible, the artefacts are identified, possibly photographed and drawn, and advice can be given on their care. For exceptional discoveries, a small excavation at the find spot may be undertaken to clarify the context of the find. Information about the object is entered on a national database and can be accessed by anyone on The Portable Antiquities Finds Database (www.finds.org.uk).

A backscattered electron image of Iron Age red glass showing dendritic copper oxide within a leaded glass matrix

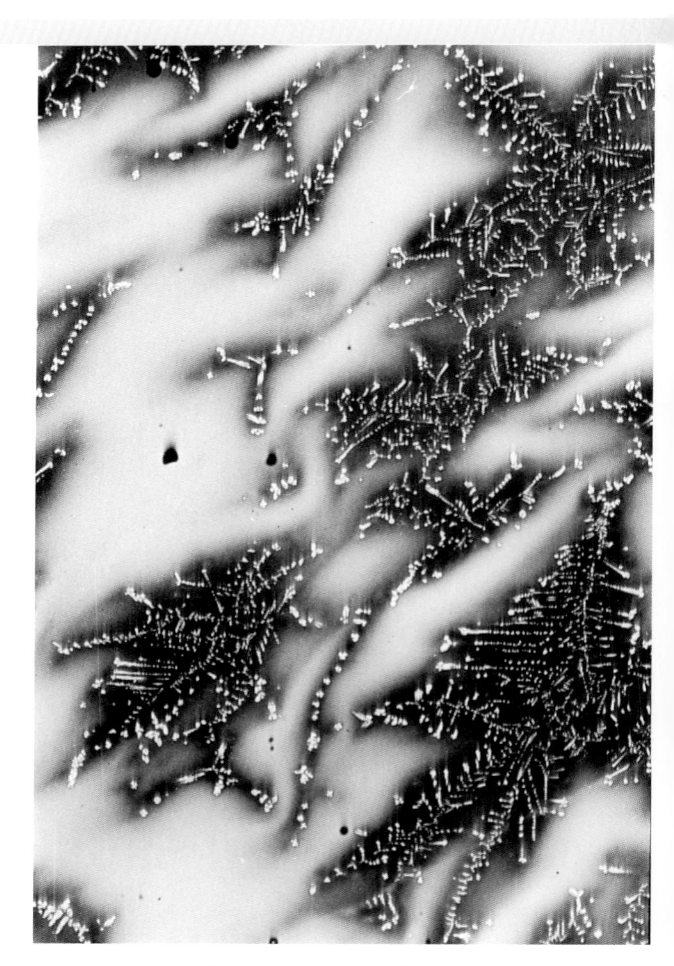

Scanning electron microscope (SEM)
Scanning electron microscopes make use of the properties of electrons rather than light to image material. The wavelength of electrons is less than 1/100th of a nanometre, far shorter than light which is 400-700 nanometres. This means that a far higher resolution and hence magnification, as well as a large depth of field, can be obtained by a microscope that uses an electron beam instead of a light beam; SEMs are regularly used to magnify samples by many thousands of times.

A beam of high energy electrons is emitted by an electron gun; this is accelerated down through a column and past a series of magnetic lenses which focuses the electron beam to a very fine spot. A set of coils is used to 'scan' the beam across the surface of the sample at a pre-determined rate.

When the electron beam hits the sample, the sample emits secondary electrons, backscattered electrons and characteristic X-rays from the surface. As the beam scans, a detector collects the electron signals. This enables an image to be built up from the number of electrons emitted from each spot on the sample, and for chemical analysis to be undertaken on the elements present.

Secondary electron images are created when loose low energy secondary electrons are knocked from the surface of the sample. Only a small amount of energy is absorbed by these electrons, which means that only those produced near the surface are detected; secondary electron images have high resolution, and are especially good for viewing the surface topography of a sample.

As well as secondary electrons, back scattered electrons can also be used to image

A secondary electron image of a pyrite mineral from Dolgellau, north Wales

specimens. When an electron from the beam encounters a nucleus in the sample, a few of these high energy electrons will be 'backscattered'. Images produced this way have some similarities to those of secondary electrons; however, the principal difference is that contrasting brightness in the image occurs in relation to the elemental composition of the specimen. In this way it is very easy to see such things as mineral inclusions in a rock matrix or inlaid material in an artefact.

The SEM can also be used for chemical analysis by measuring the characteristic X-radiation given out by atoms. When the electron beam hits an atom some electrons from within that atom are displaced. The dislodged electrons are then replaced by others, and an X-ray photon is emitted. The energy and wavelength of X-rays emitted this way is dependant on the element being 'excited', they are therefore characteristic; this enables specific and quantifiable data to be collected.

Characteristic X-ray photons can be detected either using an energy dispersive (EDX) detector, which collects and measures the number and energy for all detectable elements at once which are then displayed as a histogram of counts versus X-ray energy, or by using a wavelength dispersive spectrometer (WDX), which analyses sequentially the specific wavelength of each element present. This is more time consuming to carry out but is able to produce accurate quantitative analysis at far lower detection levels than ED analysis.

Re-conservation and restoration

How dull it is to pause, to make an end,
To rust unburnish'd, not to shine in use!
Alfred Tennyson, *Ulysses* (1842)

The ethical dilemmas of restoring historic and artistic works are well known and documented, and the arguments of proponents and opponents to restoration projects will always continue.

The United Kingdom Institute for Conservation's Code of Ethics defines restoration as: *all actions taken to modify the existing materials and structure of cultural property to represent a known earlier state. Its aim is to preserve and reveal the aesthetic and historic value of the cultural property and it is based on respect for remaining original material and clear evidence of the earlier state.*

There are no truisms in restoration; there is always an element of subjectivity in any interpretive work that lays it open for discussion and dissension. What is also a long-standing dilemma is the changing nature of ethical restoration with time and accompanying changes in fashion. The well-thought out procedures and practices of fifty years ago are often no longer acceptable today. This is partially due to our increasing analytical ability in determining 'the true nature of an object', but it is also due to our changing idea of what aspect of an object is significant. Commonplace objects of a century ago that were poorly regarded, routinely used and replaced if necessary are now rare and valuable. Their status has changed, and our attitude to them has changed accordingly, so an object may be mended, re-conserved and restored several times over the years, according to changing values and our improved scientific ability to investigate it.

Perhaps the most enduring ethical approach to restoration that is relatively free of controversy is 'the avoidance of conjecture'.

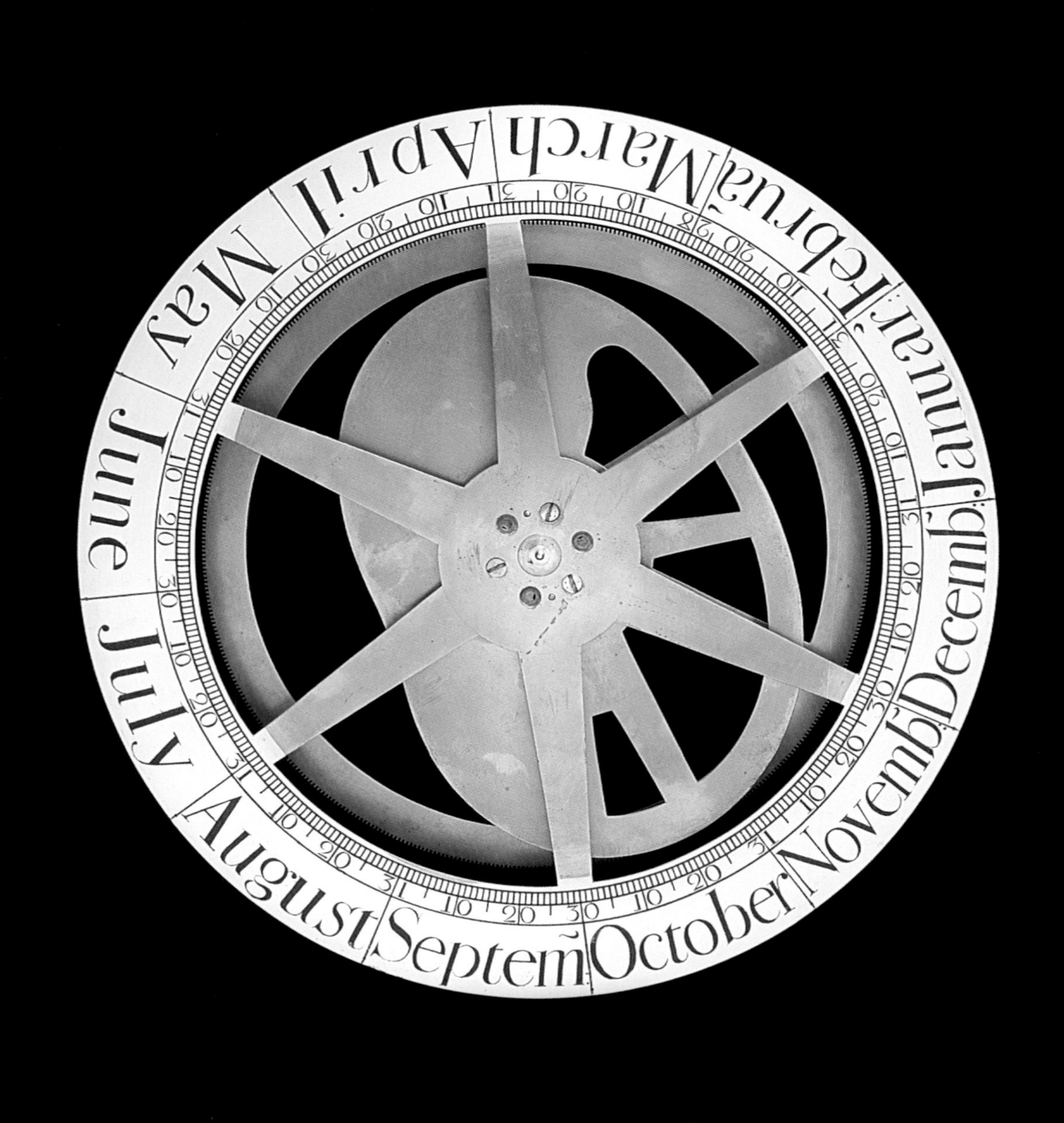
January
Februa
March
April
May
June
July
August
Septem̃
October
Novemb
Decemb

Arms and the Man
Lord Howard de Walden's collection of ancient arms and armour

Augustus John,
Thomas Evelyn Scott-Ellis, 8th Lord Howard de Walden (1880-1946), **c. 1912**

The Lord Howard de Walden collection includes a variety of objects such as swords, spearheads, arrowheads, belts, shields, sections of body armour and a number of complete helmets. The majority of these pieces are made of bronze and date from the Greek, Etruscan and Roman periods.

Thomas Evelyn Scott-Ellis, the eighth Baron Howard de Walden and fourth Baron Seaford, was born in London in 1880. He epitomised the British aristocracy of the period and is best remembered for his generous support of the arts, literature and sport, which he loved. He had a variety of interests, including a fascination for the theatre, which inspired him to write several plays. As an accomplished amateur sportsman, he distinguished himself as a member of the British Olympic fencing team at Athens in 1906.

Lord Howard de Walden was also a keen antiquarian, and put together an extensive collection of arms and armour. The collection was created not purely to demonstrate his wealth and education, but in a genuine attempt to study and record the development of arms and armour through the ages. His main area of interest was the medieval period, but his collection incorporated material from all ages and cultures, ranging in date from the eighth century BC to the seventeenth century AD.

In 1923 a catalogue of the collection was produced (Joubert 1923) in which the artefacts were described and an attempt made, based on 'the form and prevailing fashion', to assign a period and country of origin. In the introduction Lord Howard de Walden stated that he deplored the 'indifferent manner of recording the provenance of Arms and Armour in bye-gone days'. In that respect his work was pioneering, because he realized that an artefact without a record of its origins was of little value when it came to studying and interpreting the past. This belief is considered a fundamental part of any research undertaken today.

In April 1945 Lord Howard de Walden loaned the pre-classical and classical (ancient Greece, Rome and the Near East) pieces from his collection to the National Museum of Wales, with the intention that after his death they should become the property of

An Etruscan bronze helmet with applied gold decoration

the Museum and hence the nation. A year after his death in 1946, the custodianship of the collection passed to the National Museum, as he had wished.

Part of the collection was on display in the Museum until the 1960s, but no provision was made for its redisplay in the new archaeological galleries opened in 1965. The majority of the collection was then placed in storage, with a few pieces loaned to the Ashmolean Museum in Oxford for display. Interest in the collection was revived in 1990 when the British Museum approached the National Museum of Wales to request the loan of some items for a temporary exhibition on fakes. Lord Howard de Walden had believed that some of the pieces in his collection were of dubious authenticity, and research by a Russian scholar, A. A. Lessen, had found

A detail of corrosion removal

evidence to prove this. He published a paper in 1961 demonstrating that two silver gilt belts in 'Sarmatian' style and two roundels in 'Scythian' style had probably been made in a jeweller's workshop in Odessa between 1890 and 1910 (Jones 1990).

At this point it was decided that all the artefacts in the collection should be examined and their condition and authenticity re-evaluated. Today there is a host of techniques and equipment available that can be employed to do this. Visual examinations by optical microscopy and X-radiography help reveal details obscured from view or normally too small to see; they also help to deduce fabrication techniques, detect alterations and evaluate the extent of deterioration for conservation purposes. Chemical analysis techniques help identify materials and analyse their composition both qualitatively and quantitatively, while the metallographic study of a material, which involves the examination of the crystalline structure of metals and their alloys, can yield information on manufacture and construction techniques (Craddock & Bowman in Jones 1990).

The information yielded from a combination of these methods of analysis can reveal much about an artefact's construction and history. By comparing the results with data obtained from similar objects of known provenance, aspects of an artefact's history can sometimes be revealed and any forgeries detected, even if they are well disguised. None of these methods was available at the turn of the twentieth century to help Lord Howard de Walden catalogue his collection; his only guide to date and origin was the general style and outward appearance of an object.

In 1990 conservators at the National Museum of Wales surveyed the collection to assess its condition and identify which pieces were in need of treatment. The results indicated that 68 per cent of the objects were in need of conservation and out of that 14 per cent required immediate treatment to prevent disintegration. A schedule of work was therefore drawn up, and those objects at greatest risk selected for priority treatment.

The first object chosen was a bronze dome-shaped helmet with gold decoration. It was considered to be an Etruscan piece, originating from an area of north central Italy, and thought to date from around the fifth or fourth century BC.

The bronze bowl or cap-shaped helmet is richly decorated with bands of engraved and embossed gold. One band runs completely around the rim with four other bands, equally distanced apart, extending upwards to meet at the crown. A circular disc and pointed finial tops the crown. The finial was once gilded, but the majority of this has now gone, revealing the bronze beneath.

The gold was in good condition, but the bronze was covered in a rough, uneven encrustation of light green and powdery corrosion indicating that it was

X-rays of the helmet, taken from the side and from above

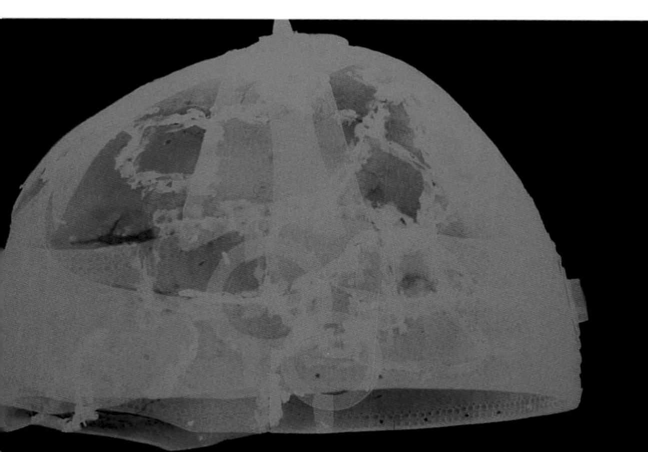

possibly suffering from 'bronze disease', where paratacamite (a basic copper chloride) is produced, which can result in a self-perpetuating corrosion cycle very destructive to copper and its alloys (Cronyn 1990). If this remained unchecked, the object would continue to weaken and possibly even start to break up. Holes and cracks in the thin bronze were visible, confirming that the structure of the object was already weak in places.

Patinas or corrosion found on metals are usually a good indication of age, and the appearance of the corrosion on the helmet indicated that this artefact had been around for a considerable length of time. The type and colour of corrosion formed depends on the composition of the alloy and the conditions in the surrounding environment. Most archaeological objects develop their distinctive patina over a considerable length of time while in the ground.

To determine the extent of the bronze disease a small section of the outer corrosion crust was removed. Bronze corrosion found on most archaeological objects retrieved from terrestrial sites normally forms a layered structure, within which the original surface detail may be preserved. However, on this object the layered structure did not exist, in fact the corrosion crust came away easily, often in large amorphous chunks to reveal what appeared to be another smooth patinated surface beneath, not the pitted and disrupted surface expected from a severely corroding object.

Prior to investigation, the authenticity of this piece had not been questioned. However, the discovery of a second patinated surface underlying the crust began to cause concern, as it indicated a less than straightforward history.

To learn more about the structure of the helmet and the condition of the metal we took a series of X-rays. These revealed a network of white lines composed of a much denser material than the bronze, and thicker than the gold decoration on the helmet. These images indicated that at some point a lead/tin soft solder had probably been used to repair and strengthen the helmet, although none of this was visible as it was hidden beneath the thick

A detail of a patch used to repair the helmet

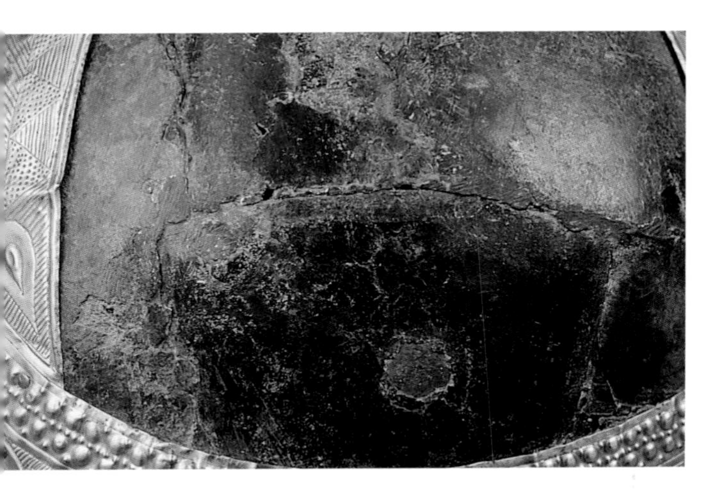

corrosion crust. Soft solder was employed in antiquity, but rarely in the construction of helmets, as any join would be a point of weakness. In this case the solder had been used to secure patches of metal in place; it had been run along cracks and used to repair breaks. The condition and method of application indicated that this solder was relatively modern; if this was the case, the corrosion above it had to be fake, applied over the top to disguise the repairs and the condition of the metal

Attempts were then made to find out more about the composition of the patina, to determine whether it was in fact artificial. For this a small sample was taken for X-ray diffraction analysis to determine the exact mineral species present. Unfortunately, the results were inconclusive; no modern pigments or additives were found and only naturally occurring copper corrosion products were detected. The green corrosion product most commonly associated with copper and its alloys is malachite (a basic copper carbonate). Since antiquity this material has also been used as a pigment, and it is quite possible that malachite, along with other copper minerals, was employed here. They would have been ground up and mixed with a binding medium, then applied like paint over the original surface to reproduce the realistic appearance of copper corrosion. However, the binding medium appears to have deteriorated over the intervening years, which would explain the powdery surface initially thought to be the result of bronze disease. The main drawback of an artificial patina is that it does not always adhere well to the surface of the object to which it has been applied, which explains why the crust fell away easily during initial investigative cleaning to reveal the original surface below.

Next, we analysed the surviving metal to establish whether the helmet was ancient. Small samples were taken from the main body of the helmet, the bronze repair patches and gold embellishment. The results indicated that the composition of the bronze of the helmet and repair patches did match that produced during the Classical period in the Mediterranean, although the metal was from at least two different sources. The gold was highly refined and its chemical composition indicated it was probably a modern addition.

Therefore, although it appears that the helmet is of classical date, and may or may not be Etruscan, it originally was a plain, dome-shaped helmet, without the addition of gold or the spike at the top. It was probably in a very poor state when originally unearthed, but complete enough to repair. Patches of metal, cut from ancient artefacts too damaged to salvage, had been used to fill the holes, and soft solder then employed to strengthen the structure and secure the patches in place. With reference to the style and decoration of the period, the helmet had been further embellished with gold, which would

The Etruscan helmet with half the false patina removed

have considerably increased the desirability and price of the object. Finally, all the unsightly repairs had been hidden under a thick layer of artificial corrosion.

This helmet was not suffering from bronze disease, as initially suspected; it was the false corrosion, not the original metal work, that was deteriorating. In order to preserve the history of this piece it was decided that the helmet should only be partially cleaned. The false corrosion on one half of the helmet has been removed to reveal the extent of the alterations and the original surface below, while on the other side the false corrosion has been preserved. The gold decoration has been kept intact because its removal might cause damage to the original surface.

The helmet is now described as a pastiche, even though a genuine helmet lies beneath the embellishment. This is because it bears no resemblance to the original, and other artefacts have been used in its reconstruction.

On discovering the alterations to the first helmet we decided to X-ray all the helmets in the collection and establish how many others had been altered. Forty pieces were examined altogether, including a few items of body armour and shields. Out of that number eighteen were original and eighteen were pastiches, three of which appear to have been based on original helmets. Of the remaining four helmets, one was a complete fake and three required further work to establish their authenticity.

Our research has now vindicated Lord Howard de Walden's suspicions concerning the authenticity of some of the pieces in his collection. Unfortunately, we have no record of how or from whom the collection was acquired. In the past, genuine artefacts were often heavily restored to improve their appearance; there were no ethical problems with stripping and repatinating a bronze to the colour thought fashionable for the period (Craddock in Jones 1990), or with reconstructing whole missing sections to create a complete object. However, in the case of some of the De Walden helmets, additions were made purely to deceive, and those who did the work had access to archaeological material, knowledge of the market and close contact with the dealers.

A variety of materials was used to create fake patinas. These include verdigris (copper acetate), which has been used as a pigment since antiquity, but its presence here is probably the result of a chemical repatination process; chrysocolla has also been identified, a naturally occurring copper silicate that when ground produces a pigment similar in colour to malachite. Further minerals identified included gypsum (calcium sulphate), barytes (barium sulphate), azurite (a blue coloured basic copper carbonate) and paratacamite. It appears that pigments were probably being mixed with materials such as gypsum or barytes and used as fillers, or applied over repairs to form a thick crust that was capable of disguising the alterations.

To understand why such a high percentage of the collection are pastiches we have to look at the trade in antiquities at the time. Lord Howard de Walden was purchasing antiquities at the turn of the twentieth century, when demand was high and often exceeded the supply. The production of fake artefacts flourished in the nineteenth century, but the industry was already well established and had been in existence for several hundred years before then.
In the seventeenth and eighteenth centuries those who went on the Grand Tour were encouraged to return home with souvenirs from their journeys.

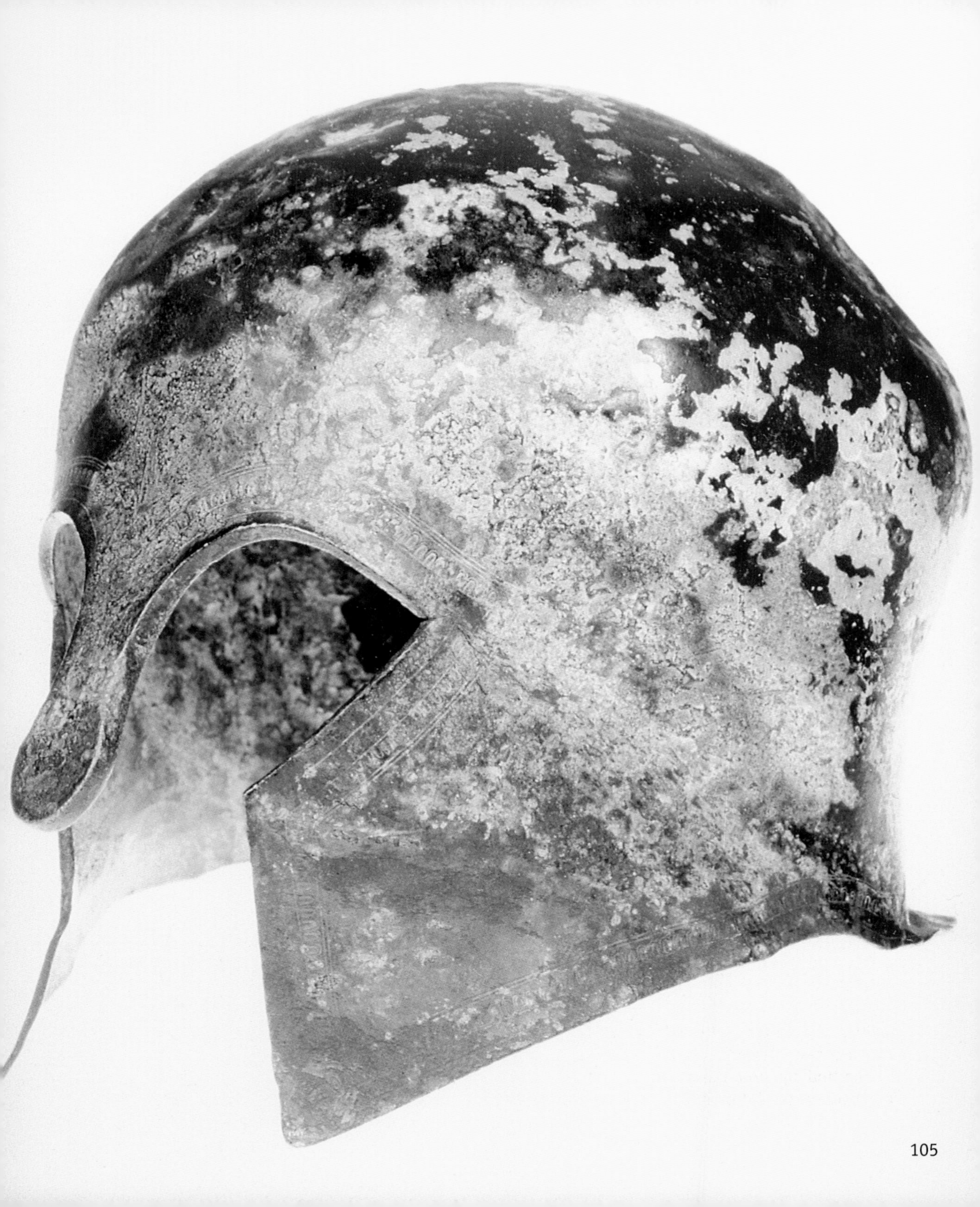

An Athenian red-figure cup from Etruria showing a Greek helmet (© Altenburg Staatliches Lindenau-Museum)

Even then warnings were given to potential buyers regarding unscrupulous dealers, as the demand for ancient artefacts had made the production of fakes a lucrative business (Jones 1990).

However, Lord Howard de Walden did manage to collect some wonderful examples of ancient metal work. His collection includes a number of fine Corinthian type helmets that were worn by the Greek hoplite soldiers in the fifth and sixth centuries BC, which are often found depicted on Greek sculpture and pottery from the period (Warry 1980). X-rays of these objects reveal that most have escaped any serious attempts at alteration or repair.

After discovering the true nature of some of the pieces in the collection, we had to decide how best to treat the collection as a whole. None of the alterations made to genuine artefacts will be reversed unless they are causing a problem with stability, and all the pastiches will be preserved in their present state.

The findings from the research will have quite an impact on the future display and interpretation of this collection. The collection as a whole, including the objects identified as pastiches, tells a fascinating story about the pitfalls of collecting artefacts in the first quarter of the twentieth century. The pastiches found in the Lord Howard de Walden collection probably also represent the last flourish in production because, by the 1930s, fashion changed and the demand for antiquities fell. This is a gentleman's collection that tells us as much about the beginning of the twentieth century as it does about the arms and armour of the ancient world.

Penny Hill

CRONYN, J. M. 1990. *The Elements of Archaeological Conservation*. Routledge, London.

JONES, M. (ed.). 1990. *FAKE? The Art of Deception*. British Museum Publications Ltd., London.

JOUBERT, F. 1923. *Catalogue of the Collection of Arms and Armour formed by Lord Howard de Walden*. H & W Brown, London.

WARRY, J. 1980. *Warfare in the Classical World*. Salamander Books Ltd, London.

Langite

Wroewolfeite

XRD

X-ray diffraction, known by its acronym XRD, is a technique used in the identification of crystalline substances, particularly minerals. Crystalline material has an internal ordered arrangement of atoms. When a crystal is exposed to an incident X-ray beam, diffraction will occur in specific directions related to the atomic structure and orientation of the crystals. Every crystalline mineral generates a unique pattern of diffraction and in XRD analysis a recording of this pattern is compared to a reference database. Matching a known database pattern to the measured pattern enables an accurate identification of the material to be made. As well as being used in mineralogy, XRD is also used in other disciplines requiring the identification of crystalline substances, for example corrosion products or pigments.

Some minerals are particularly difficult to identify, especially dimorphus substances where two minerals have exactly the same chemical composition. Some dimorphs such as graphite and diamond are easily distinguished by their appearance, however others such as langite and wroewolfeite, which both have the chemical formula $Cu_4(SO_4)(OH)_6.2H_2O$, can be difficult to tell apart as they are of similar appearance and cannot be positively identified by compositional analysis. Difficult dimorphous pairs of substances like this can quickly be identified and distinguished by the XRD technique, because it characterises them on the basis of their distinct and unique crystal structure.

Moving a medieval church
Re-erecting St Teilo's Church

St Teilo's Church on its original site, before dismantling

The collection of re-erected buildings at St Fagans comprises a cross-section of building types including houses, cottages, farm buildings, craft workshops, mills, a baker's, a post office, a school, a workmen's institute and places of worship. Our Historic Buildings Unit is responsible for dismantling, transporting and re-erecting these buildings. This specialist Unit includes carpenters, painters and masons with traditional craft and trade skills, who have also acquired knowledge of essential conservation techniques. Buildings and structures are not accepted for removal to the Museum unless threatened with demolition or collapse. Their rescue is a means of ensuring their future.

The re-erection and refurbishment of the medieval church of St Teilo from Llandeilo Tal-y-bont is one of our most ambitious projects to-date. Not only does it represent the first church of its kind to be moved to a British open-air museum, its importance as a building has also enabled us to explore new and exciting approaches to research and interpretation.

The church, which is believed to have been built during the eleventh century on the site of an earlier pre-Norman church, originally stood close to the banks of the river Llwchwr at Llandeilo Tal-y-bont near Pontarddulais in south Wales. Abandoned in 1970, it was scheduled as an Ancient Monument by Cadw. Following lengthy discussions involving local authorities and the Church in Wales, it was decided that the already decaying church could not be saved in situ. It was therefore offered to the Museum in 1984, and permission was granted by Cadw in 1985 to dismantle the church and re-erect it at St Fagans.

In 1985, the careful process of recording and dismantling the structure began. Dismantling was considerably delayed by the discovery of two major series of pre-Reformation wall-paintings along with two later schemes, numerous texts and areas of decorative patterns, all of which had to be carefully recorded, removed and conserved. There were several layers to some of these wall-paintings, but the scheme created around 1520 is now being studied so that it can be reproduced on the walls of the re-erected church to give an impression of the internal decoration of the building at that time. The original paintings are fairly fragmentary and are currently in storage (although they can be viewed by arrangement).

The process of dismantling the building can be viewed as a form of above-ground archaeology. The removal of layers of lime-wash to uncover the wall paintings provided the Historic Buildings Unit with vital clues as to the date of the original structure and subsequent additions. In the same way, the removal of lime-wash and render from the exterior walls enabled the team to uncover hidden features such as blocked-up window openings and added Victorian features.

The church after removal of the lime-wash layers. Note the original window on the right and a later, Victorian addition on the left

Students from Cardiff University Conservation Department removing the wall-paintings

Recording the structure so that it could be re-assembled at the Museum required careful and precise documentation. First, all significant masonry features – quoins, windows, corners, lintels and steps – were identified by means of a letter code to distinguish them. Each individual stone was then given a specific number. Different colours were used to distinguish between external and internal features and particular internal features such as the various arcade arches. Once this had been done, the roof timbers were numbered, though here, instead of painting numbers onto the surfaces, numbered brass tags were fixed to the main faces.
To record the building, two horizontal datum lines were set out at right angles to one another, at a

An example of the notes taken on site while recording the building

An archaeological dig on the original site, once the church had been dismantled to ground level

height of about 1,200 mm above ground level. A vertical datum line was established at the point where the first two lines intersected. Each point of the structure could then be measured off these three lines. These measurements were augmented by hundreds of photographs as well as notes and sketches. In addition to the record photographs, a detailed photogrammetric survey was carried out. Using special rectified photography, it was possible to produce images that were not distorted by perspective and could be used to produce accurate scaled elevational detail.

Any discrepancies or original mistakes in the structure have to be reproduced in the re-erected building. We like to boast that we can accurately re-erect a building to within 10 mm of its original dimensions! The evidence gleaned from this process, together with the results of an archaeological excavation of the remaining foundations, answered a number of key questions about the development and plan of the church. This information was essential to enable the church to be reconstructed accurately in its early sixteenth-century form.

The first identifiable structure was almost certainly a two-cell church consisting of a nave and chancel, thought to be thirteenth-fourteenth century in date, a pattern that was standard at this time. The north and south transepts were probably added about a century later. Both are of similar masonry construction, and correspond to the dating of a painting on the east wall of the south transept. It is thought that the extension of the south transept westwards to form an aisle occurred during the late fifteenth century, the old south wall being replaced by an arcade of two arches, with arches also being created to the transepts. The final addition to the

A plan of the church

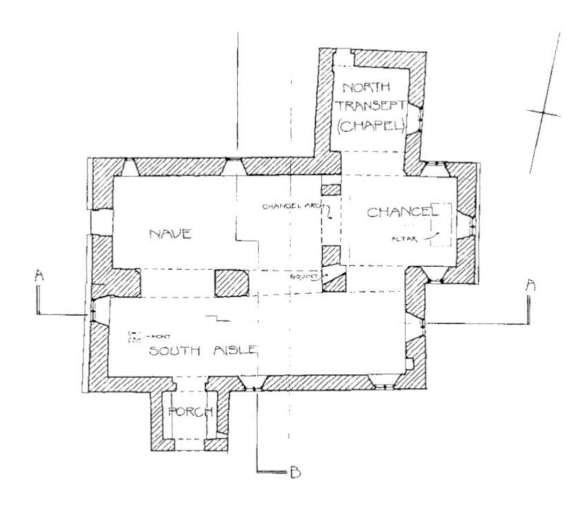

church was a porch leading to the south aisle.

Detailed architectural and archaeological research of this kind forms a sound basis for an accurate reconstruction. However, far more is needed before the building can qualify as a relevant and meaningful exhibit that can educate, inform, entertain and appeal to visitors at all levels.

As early as 1916, the important link between church architecture in Wales and historical research was established by The Rev. E. Tyrrell-Green. He wrote:

The study of Architecture would be a profitless employment unless constant reference is made to the beliefs, the customs, the feelings and the aspirations of the times and places where styles of Architecture arose, while, on the other hand, the historian can never afford to neglect Architecture, for this is no mere pastime, but the record of a people's life and character in an abiding form, which cannot lie. Into their Architecture, nations, in all ages, have put themselves; into their sacred Architecture they have put their best selves.

It was decided to rebuild and refurbish the church as it would have appeared around 1520. We can use the architectural clues from this period, found during the dismantling process, as keys to understanding the social, religious and political history from which the church was constructed and furnished. The period chosen follows closely the extension of the south transept westwards to form the south aisle, presumably to accommodate a larger congregation. It can be argued that this fits in well with the greater economic recovery in Wales after the establishment of the Welsh Tudor Dynasty in the late fifteenth century, which brought with it a period of relative calm after long stretches of political and social unrest. Glanmor Williams (1962) links architectural development to this economic recovery, and refers to it as 'The urge to build and beautify ... there was hardly a church in Wales, in however remote or bare a parish, which could not boast some degree of reconstruction or refurbishing.' Clues found inside the church can also be used to illuminate the nature of worship during the period up to 1520. First, and most important, are the pre-Reformation wall-paintings discovered under later lime-wash. These depict various themes from the life of Christ along with many saints including Saint Catherine and Saint Christopher. Wall-paintings such as these have been described as 'the poor man's Bible', designed to interpret scenes from the Bible to an illiterate congregation, but also crafted to instil a sense of awe, fear and obedience, and constantly remind the worshippers of the inevitability of death, the Divine Judgement and Retribution.

A conserved wall-painting, showing the Mocking of Christ before the crucifixion

Second are the rood screen and loft, evidence for which was found in the form of an access doorway and corbel stones in the masonry work of the chancel arch. Both wall-paintings, rood screen and loft would have been brightly painted. Siôn Cent, a medieval poet described a painter painting images of this kind:

A phaentiwr delw a phwyntel,
Yn paentiaw delwau lawer,
A llu o saint â lliw sêr.

(A painter of images with his brush
Painting many images,
And a host of saints with the colour of stars.)
(Williams 1962)

Thus, even if the congregation did not understand the messages of the sermons, the impact of the paintings, the mysticism of the rood screen, the repetition of the mass and fear surrounding the power of the clergy must have been enough to keep them going to church.

Displaying the church as it would have appeared in the early sixteenth century meant sifting through the evidence in order to identify those features and details that belonged to that period, and might have to be replicated if they were missing.

One fourteenth-century two-light window still survived in the south wall. It was reasonably complete, though a few sections in the central mullion were in extremely poor condition and part of the sill was missing. To repair or replace these sections it was necessary first to identify the original stone used, and to find out, if possible, where this would have been quarried. The stone was identified as being Cae-ras conglomerate (Lower Devonian brownstone containing small quartz pebbles and other stones including Silurian sandstone and siltstones with fossils), a bed of which ran quite close to the site of the church. This stone was also used for the eleventh-century font that stood at the west end of the aisle. A long-abandoned section of Cil-yr-ychen quarry near Llandybie (about nine miles up-river from Llandeilo Tal-y-bont) yielded several

Conservation work on a single-light trefoil head window in the north wall of the nave

An example of a carved tracery fragment found during the dismantling process and a newly carved section

large stones of identical composition and colour to the window stones. These were cut to shape and used to replace missing sections of masonry in the window. This quarry may also have provided the limestone used for the production of lime for use in mortars, renders and lime-wash in the church. Identical conservation work was also carried out on a single-light trefoil head window in the north wall.

Most traces of the later (fifteenth-century) windows had been removed, possibly by the Victorians. None of the mullions and tracery remained in situ, and while most of the window openings could still be identified, only one, at the east end of the south aisle, still retained its original sill, head and external label. Fortunately, during the dismantling process, several sections of carved tracery were found. When re-assembled, they formed a two-light cinquefoil window head which fitted the window opening in the south aisle perfectly.

This pattern was then used for the other openings, for both single and two-light windows. The original stone used for these carved sections was Sutton stone, quarried at Aber-Ogwr in the Vale of Glamorgan. Unfortunately, these reserves were largely exhausted by the late Middle Ages and the quarries were abandoned. The best match, in terms of composition, texture and colour, was found in Portland stone from Dorset and this was used to replicate the missing sections.

We know that some of the roof timbers had been replaced in the past. Those in the nave were dated

A new, two-light window, formed using the pattern of the original fragments

using dendrochronology to 1732, while the trusses in the chancel were renewed in 1890 when the east gable wall was totally rebuilt, complete with cast-iron lancet window. In December 2002, the timbers from the south aisle were examined with a view to also dating these by dendrochronology. Unfortunately, the timbers were found to have insufficient tree rings to enable an accurate assessment to be carried out.

Stylistically, the trusses were of medieval appearance; certainly the designs and mouldings were correct for the period. The question that then arose was whether they would be strong enough to support the weight of a stone-tiled roof. To assess this a programme of stress-testing of the timbers was commissioned. In spite of the fact that many of the trusses and collars had been damaged by exposure to the weather and insect attack, the tests demonstrated that, with repairs, they could be re-used.

Where timbers were missing, as in the case of one of the trusses in the north chapel, or where surviving timbers were of recent date (as in the chancel), replica oak trusses were made to match the originals. Likewise, any repairs carried out were also made to blend in with the original materials and mouldings.

The original roof was stone-tiled, and pieces of tile had been found in the wall surrounding the graveyard. Over the years we have collected thousands of such tiles, and these are being used to re-roof the church. The ridges would have been covered with glazed clay ridge tiles. Several fragments and one complete example were found on the site, and after discussions with archaeologists, we commissioned replica hand-made clay tiles to match the originals.

It is important to remember that the church was used as a religious building up until its ultimate abandonment in 1970. Members of the community that used to worship in the church still have strong and important memories of their time as a congregation. Material from the church's recent past provides important photographic and oral history evidence that will be kept in our audio-visual archive.

The church has taken many years to re-erect; it is a complex and time-consuming project, and one of several currently being undertaken at St Fagans. A small exhibition has been set up next to the church to explain the work being done there, and an interpreter gives daily guided tours to visitors, who can enter the building site and see at first hand the nature of the project and learn about the church's past, present and future.

The re-erection of the church at St Fagans is but another phase in its history, where visitors in the twenty-first century will play just as important a role as did the Medieval pilgrims!

Sioned Wyn Hughes and Gerallt Nash

TYRRELL-GREEN, Rev. E. 1916-17. The Church Architecture of Wales. *Transactions of the Honourable Society of Cymmrodorion,* 52-119.

WILLIAMS, G. 1962. *The Welsh Church from Conquest to Reformation*. University of Wales Press, Cardiff.

Replica oak trusses, matching the original medieval pattern, being made with traditional hand tools

An original glazed clay ridge tile

Resolving the 'Equation of Time'
Thomas Tompion's Iscoed Park clock

The Iscoed Park Tompion clock

The collections at St Fagans contain a range of clocks from different periods of history. One of these is the Iscoed Park long-case clock by Thomas Tompion (1639-1713). This clock is a complex composite object both from a constructional point of view, and for its period. The first decade of the eighteenth century was at the cutting edge of knowledge, design and craftsmanship both for the manufacture of the mechanisms and for the cases of clocks. During this period, Thomas Tompion, known as the Father of Horology, was at the top of his trade, and his reputation has remained undiminished.

The Iscoed Park clock dates from around 1710. Most of Tompion's mechanisms carry a serial number, except those pieces made for royal ownership or noteworthy from a design point of view, and where such numbering would probably be of no benefit. This timepiece, and its sister clock at the Pump House in Bath, are of this latter type and therefore their precise date of manufacture is not known.

The long-case clock was purchased by the Museum in 1989 from the Godsal family of Iscoed Park, Flintshire, who had owned the clock for at least 170 years. Its location in 1818, (known because of a surviving receipt detailing remedial work carried out on the mechanism to return it to working order), was in Oxford Street, London. Therefore the clock has been moved several times during its working life and has possibly had a number of owners.

There are complex ethical issues concerning the conservation of working objects in museum collections, and the field of horological conservation can contribute much to this debate. Horological mechanisms are scientific instruments, but they were often 'dressed-up' for visual impact within cases that are regarded as pieces of furniture in their own right. The conservation of objects such as long-case clocks

An engraving of Thomas Tompion, c. 1700s (© Science Museum)

therefore requires consideration of the materials used for their manufacture, their aesthetic nature and their use; and it is impossible to take into account all these aspects without introducing some degree of compromise to their long term preservation.

The dilemma with a functioning clock is usually whether it should be set to work or not. Leaving the mechanism stationary will not preserve its ability to run in the future; however, the continual working of such a mechanism without constant attention will result in its rapid deterioration. Therefore, the compromise that suggests itself is to set the mechanism to work, but in a controlled way, so the prevention of wear becomes the primary consideration. This in turn results in a shift of emphasis from its original purpose, where efficiency in keeping time on a daily basis was its foremost function. If this compromise is applied carefully, running the clock can become a method for the object's conservation, instead if its deterioration. The Iscoed Park clock had not run for a number of years. Returning it to working order was seen as a means of improving our understanding of the mechanism, as well as being the best method of preserving it.

Before working on any such instrument from the eighteenth century, the early period of horology, it is important to have an understanding of the maker's design and working practices and what level of craftsmanship was applied in its manufacture. These early timepieces still bore the manufacturer's individual 'fingerprint', and therefore identifying later additions or other such changes are an important precursor to any conservation treatment, and should help to provide a consistent ethical approach to any interventive conservation undertaken.

The horological mechanism and its case can be viewed as one object since they both share the same provenance and period, and complement each other, even though made by different craftsmen from separate trades. Although in function and material terms many aspects differ, a more holistic approach does help to achieve a balanced view of the degree of intervention necessary in any one area. Historically it is rare to find a clock where its mechanism and case have both received the same level of consideration in terms of their maintenance.

This point was made some years ago by the National Portrait Gallery, which put on an exhibition of frames with the paintings removed (*The Art of the Picture Frame,* 1996-1997). The implication was that many frames are as worthy of notice as the paintings themselves, but that an extreme approach to their display was required to illustrate this fact.

The kidney-shaped cam that controls the equation of time pointer

The mechanism with the top plate removed. The striking train, introduced later, is on the left

The mechanism

The Tompion clock is termed as an 'equation of time' clock, designed to show the time of day (in both minutes and hours), the day of the month and the 'equation of time': the difference between local solar time as shown by a sundial and the constant time kept by the clock dial. This is expressed as plus or minus so many minutes, dependent on what day of the year the dial is viewed. Prior to the advent of the railways and the introduction of timetables, people used local solar time, which would have meant, for instance, that Cardiff was several minutes behind London time. The clock also strikes the hour to the number of the hour.

Tompion introduced a high degree of accuracy in the manufacture of clocks, together with supportive mechanisms that imply concern not only with the accuracy of timekeeping, but also with the longevity or even the conservation of the materials he used.

The use of brass and steel in the mechanism is interesting from a conservation point of view. Clockmakers from an early period recognized the wearing properties of both brass and steel. Brass is more malleable and would be expected to wear first; in fact, the reverse is true for this clock mechanism, since its use is confined to the driving wheels and the steel is used for the running pinions. This careful placing of the appropriate metal and accurate cutting of meshing teeth results in minimum wear. Similarly, there is a running counterpoise weight attached to the equation pointer, again, to reduce stress on the mechanism.

The case

The case, which has to form a rigid stand for the mechanism, has also been designed with consideration for its function. Any physical movement of the case, by external contact, loose joints or loose anchorage to the wall, would bring the mechanism to a stop.

The Tompion clock case was designed to be rigid, a factor often missing in other cases. The mechanism is bracketed on both sides onto the backboards, instead of relying only on the anchorage of the seatbed. The seatbed also has a raised well to 'contain' the mechanism plates. The quality of the construction of the backboard is of as high a standard as the visible components, demonstrating that Tompion recognized that the quality of workmanship, and therefore the long term stability of the piece, was of importance in terms of the longevity of the mechanism's working life.

The hood door carries a pane of glass just under two feet high. This was a very large sheet for the standard production of clear glass at the time. An added complication is that this clock is one of the first examples anywhere in the world of a domed shaped dial. This meant that this very large pane of glass had to be cut to form shoulders needed for this shape. The process of cutting and handling the glass would have been precarious, especially with such an expensive commodity. To the early eighteenth century viewer looking at this clock, it is possibly the size and shape of the glass pane which would have impressed them first; whereas to today's eyes it has no great significance.

The Bath Tompion clock

The Bath clock

Initial investigative work on the Iscoed Park clock was made in order to appreciate the degree of wear, deterioration, disfigurement, previous conservation or restoration work and any additions or subtractions to the object. The closest existing Tompion clock to this example is on public display at the Pump Rooms in Bath, and this was examined for comparison.

Towards the end of his working life, Tompion became ill and spent some time 'taking the waters' at Bath. At the end of this period he donated a 'month going equation timepiece' together with a sundial to the city. It even has a mention in Charles Dickens' *Pickwick Papers:* 'The Great Pump Room is a spacious saloon, ornamented with Corinthian pillars, and a music-gallery, and a Tompion clock...' (chapter 36).

This clock is a virtual sister clock to the Iscoed Park clock, although there are visible differences. The Bath clock has an oak case with a translucent finish, while the Iscoed Park clock is ebonized, with gilt decoration applied, and this finish can be loosely termed as 'japanned'. There is no other known example of a japanned or lacquered case by Tompion, and so it was presumed that the ebonized finish had been added at a later date, and that the Iscoed Park clock had begun life looking like the Bath clock. However, close examination showed that the lacquer was not directly applied to the oak, but instead to an interleaving veneer of pear wood; all the shaped mouldings were also built up from solid pear wood. The case manufacturer must have set out deliberately to construct this finish, since pear wood's finer grain is much more appropriate than the coarse, open grain of oak for receiving a decorative finish. This type of finish could possibly make Tompion's Iscoed Park clock unique.

Compound moulding showing the 'built-up' nature of oak substrate and pear wood facing

The condition of the case

The hood was structurally the weakest component of the entire case and required remedial work to re-attach its left side. It became apparent that a small caddy top decorative piece had been removed from the hood; its point of attachment was still visible due to the remains of the original glue line.

The case had also been shortened at the base where a complete section of the plinth had been removed and replaced with a much shallower piece made of pine – the only piece of softwood in the entire case. There was some evidence of woodworm in the base moulding, which had been covered over with gilding at a later date. Infilling of the decorative finish on the plinth and base is substantial and this was possibly required as a result

The clock's hands.
Note the sun graphic on
the equation pointer

The clock's face

of damp conditions. Its extent could be clearly seen by the variation in fluorescence when examined under ultraviolet light.

The inside surface of the case had been completely 'finished' when new in order to seal in the open grain of the oak carcass. This helped to prevent the transfer of moisture and therefore slowed down the reaction rate of the timber to both humid and dry conditions.

Inside the hood and covering the inside of the tambour top was a cotton cloth glued to the 'staves'. This would have acted as both a structural support for the coopered top, but also, if shrinkage of the staves occurred, would have provided a measure of dust proofing to prevent dust reaching the mechanism.

The cotton cloth that once lined the inside of the internal dome on the hood is now missing and the only evidence that it existed are the remains of its woven pattern preserved as an impression in the animal glue and as a few twisted threads in the encrusted adhesive. However, this is enough to make a good match for the type and quality of the original cloth. As this area has been protected from pollutants and physical damage since new, it remains the only area where the original pigment can be seen on the inside of the case. With this in mind, we decided to place a polyester film over the area rather than to replace the cloth; this meant the remaining pigment was protected but still visible.

There was considerable loss of applied gilded decoration over the entire case. However, the overall design was still discernible by examining adjacent areas or those mirrored on symmetrical areas, enabling accurate restoration of the damaged areas to be carried out to a limited degree.

The contrast between the lighter linear gilding of

the central column and the heavier gilding of the spiral decoration and panel work is a subtlety that should be preserved. However, the gilding on the front of the case had begun to appear a dull oxidised yellow with a crystalline appearance, and this had reduced its contrast in appearance to the ebonized background. Analytical tests on samples of the surface finish of the case by FTIR confirmed that a shellac based spirit polish had been used.
Visual inspection also suggested a burnished finish using an oil as a lubricant; this was deduced by the tell-tale signs of an undulating viscous effect instead of a pared down pumiced finish. Since the main discolouration was to the front of the case, it seems likely that the catalytic effect of ultraviolet light had taken its toll. The compatibility of the spirit solvent used in the restoration of the finish makes re-emulsifying the original polish a delicate process but does allow the consolidation, stability and visual integrity of the finish to be achieved without changing its nature. A denatured spirit-based finish will often react well to re-emulsifying. After testing, the original contrast was restored with no discernable detrimental effect to the adhesion of the gilded design.

Conservation of the clock

The clock dial plate has applied chapter rings, which are silvered brass. Through repeated handling the silver had worn away to reveal the underlying brass plate. Invoices that were acquired with the clock indicate that there had been several attempts at re-silvering these, and this seems to have been perceived as a part of the normal maintenance process – as with changing the main steel drive cables. The chapter rings needed re-silvering to prevent further tarnishing and to improve their visual appearance. After silvering, a lacquer was applied to help protect the new surface.

The mechanism was also dismantled, recorded and photographed. Weakened springs were re-tensioned, missing linkage pins replaced and bent ones set true. The equation counterbalance, which was set on the incorrect side of the pulley, was set right and the frayed main drive steel cable (from the 1950s) was replaced with a new cable of equal diameter. The whole movement was cleaned and oiled and then re-assembled with adjustments made to the alignment of the motion work to allow the clock to strike precisely on the hour.

The earliest dated mark on the clock was scratched on the back of the main chapter ring – 'This face cleaned by Geo Allen 1796', the latest was scratched on the striking side of the mechanism – 'G Parker 1977 Oswestry'. These are but two of the long line of people to have cleaned and worked on the mechanism over its 300-year history.

There seems to be some disparity between the way the mechanism and the case have been treated and dealt with in the past. Much thought, time and effort have been applied to any additions and adaptation to the mechanism, while the case has received less consideration, and no records exist of previous work carried out on this component. As a decision had been made not to reverse any previous work to the mechanism, the case was treated similarly. Its base was not rebuilt or its caddy top replaced. Restoration could have been achieved by copying the design of its sister clock in Bath, but the two clocks do differ in detail, and so it was felt more appropriate to leave the case in its historically altered state.

The very existence of the Bath clock has a bearing on the need for any restoration work to the

Iscoed Park clock, since they both have separate histories to reflect. One has been on public view since its manufacture by Tompion, and the other has spent its life in private hands and in more than one residence. The Iscoed Park clock's long-term preservation should arguably be seen to reflect its entire history and working life, and viewed in direct comparison to its sister clock at Bath.

This brings us back to the question of the working mechanism. When the British Museum last overhauled the Bath clock they were surprised to find, after nearly 300 years of virtually continuous working, how little wear was perceptible. This is both a vindication of Tompion's own skill and his choice of materials, and a tribute to those who worked on the clock's maintenance. This fact in turn presents a positive outlook for the future working of the Iscoed Park clock. If the mechanism is to be put to work once again, the weakest points, as built into the working train by Tompion, should become the monitoring points; and it is the condition of these weakest points that should dictate whether the mechanism should be set to work or not.

The reasoning behind the clock's manufacture was that it would show accurate local time by continuously showing the divergence of sun time from mean time. To preserve its original purpose there is an argument that if the clock is to work on public display once again it should possibly show the local time according to its geography, rather than showing the present Greenwich Mean Time. To do this effectively there would need to be a sundial sited nearby for reference. The clock could become a powerful educational tool for understanding the nature of time, by which we all have to live.

Emyr Davies

SYMONDS, R. W. 1951. *Thomas Tompion, His Life and Work*. Batsford, London.

LOOMES, B. 1985. *Grandfather clocks and their cases.* Arco Pub, New York.

STALKER, J. 1960. *A treatise of japanning and varnishing, 1688*. Tiranti, London.

The equation of time, showing how a sun dial is fast or slow at different times of the year compared with an accurate clock (after Waugh 1973)

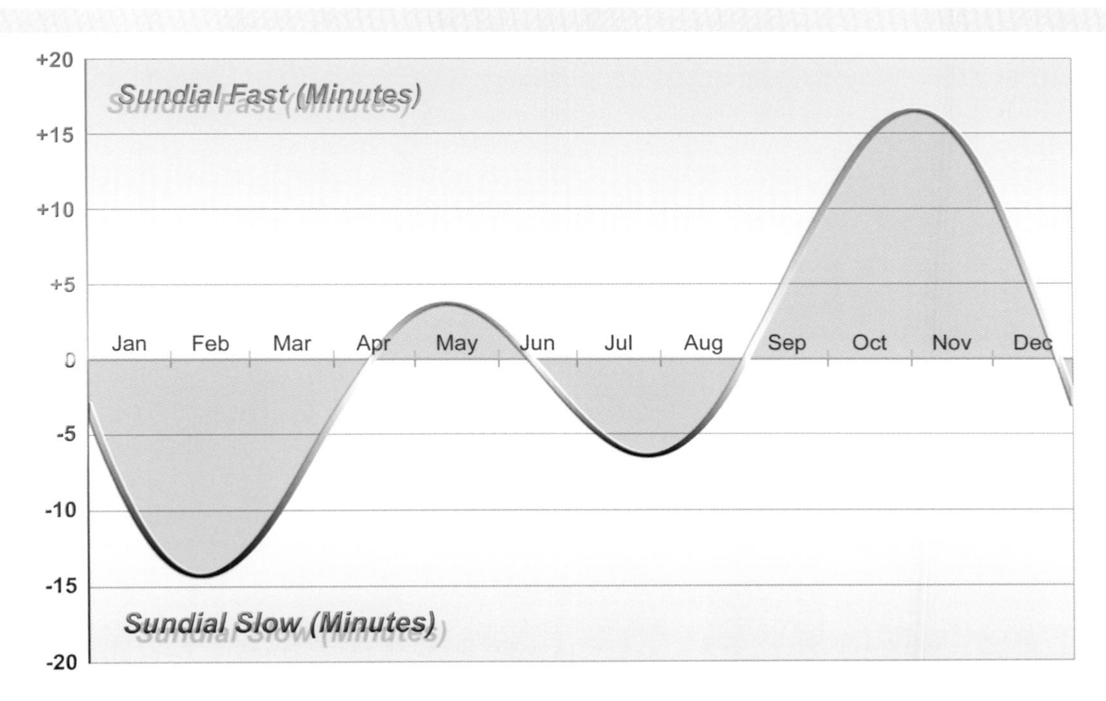

The equation of time

The Tompion clock is termed an 'equation of time' clock which, as well as being a precise clock dividing every day of the year into exactly 24 hours, also shows the precise 'solar time'. Solar time is the time indicated by a sundial, which always shows noon when the sun reaches its local zenith. The length of a solar day from one sundial noon to the next varies throughout the year. The equation of time clock can give the solar time every day of the year, even though solar time differs from 'clock time' by continuously varying amounts throughout the year. This is primarily due to the elliptical orbit of the Earth around the Sun and the tilt of the Earth's rotational axis. Solar time is behind local clock time in February and July, but ahead of it in May and November. The relationship between clock time and solar time is shown graphically above.

WAUGH, A. E. 1973. *Sundials. Their theory and construction*. Dover Publications Inc., New York.

A tale of two paintings
A technical examination of *The Poulterer's Shop*

***The Poulterer's Shop*, before cleaning**

The Poulterer's Shop by Frans Snyders was allocated to the National Museum of Wales by HM Government in lieu of Inheritance Tax in 1998. It had been in a British collection since the early nineteenth century. The attribution to Frans Snyders and Rubens's studio had been made on stylistic grounds, as the painting is not signed. It is painted in oil on canvas and was thought to date from about 1610.

At the time of acquisition it was found to be in relatively good condition for a painting of its age. The original linen support is made up of two pieces seamed together down the right-hand side of the composition. The width of the left-hand piece, 1,240 mm, probably represents the maximum loom width available at this period, hence the necessity of stitching an additional piece of material to it to make up the required size. This canvas support had later been relined onto a similar cloth using a glue-paste adhesive. The relining had been carried out to repair the two tears sustained by the original canvas, one in the face of the old man at the upper right and the other at centre bottom of the composition. The support was in sound condition, although the relining treatment had caused the vertical seam to appear more prominently at the surface, and the various losses along its length had been filled and retouched. Original tacking margins are often found to have been removed prior to relining, but in this case the upper margin was retained and the presence of unpainted canvas here is a clear indication that the ground layer was applied in the artist's studio after the canvas had been stretched up, as was usual at this period. As well as the discoloured retouches to the tear damages, the vertical edges were considerably retouched and there were minor retouches in the upper background and around the depiction of a girl's arm and sleeve. A thick, yellowed resin varnish covered the whole of the composition, obscuring the brilliance of the original colours.

Shortly after acquisition, a decision was taken to remove the varnish coating, revarnish the painting and replace the discoloured retouches. During this treatment a full technical investigation was carried out, which included examination of the painting in infrared light and with X-radiography, as well as under a high powered microscope. Small paint samples were also taken to assess the layer structure of the painting.

The painting has always been regarded as the joint production of two artists: Frans Snyders, who painted the still-life components, and one of Peter Paul Rubens's assistants, possibly Arnout Vinckenborch (Vlieghe 1987), who painted the figures and background. Our findings provide a fascinating insight into the history of the painting and the methods of the artists involved in this collaboration.

Frans Snyders was an acknowledged master of still-life painting in his day. He specialized in the representation of fruit, flowers and vegetables, as well as birds and animals, both alive and dead. Born in Antwerp in 1579, he became a pupil of Jan Breughel the Younger in 1592. By 1602 he was a Master Painter and he subsequently travelled to Italy where he is recorded as active in 1608. By 1609 he had returned to Antwerp and two years later married the sister of his fellow painters the de Vos brothers. He continued to live and work in the same city until his death in 1657.

Peter Paul Rubens returned from Italy to Antwerp in 1608, where he set up a large and active studio and, with the help of his pupils, handled many large commissions. There is documentary evidence to show that Rubens also collaborated with independent

Details from the chicken's head and the woman's face

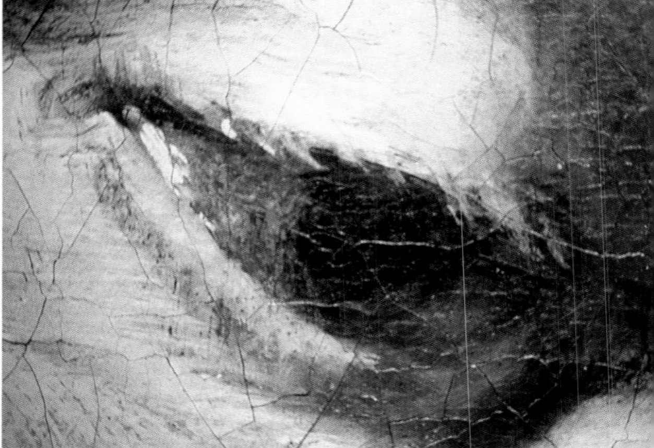

artists such as Frans Snyders, Jan Wildens and Jan Breughel the Elder, wherever their specialist capabilities were required for the composition in hand. In particular, he employed Snyders to paint the animals and plants in many of his paintings of mythological subjects and hunting scenes in the period 1610-1637 (Robels 1989).

Although it is not always possible to distinguish the individual work of Rubens's pupils in the joint studio productions, because they closely imitated Rubens's style, the hands of Rubens's fellow master painters are easier to recognise as they each had a distinctive manner of their own. Snyders, in particular, has a sharp, detailed method of paint application, very different from the free and rather sketchy brushwork of Rubens. This characteristic can clearly be observed in *The Poulterer's Shop,* where the bold and loose style of the figures and background contrasts strongly with the minutely detailed rendering of the birds' feathers and the leaves of the vegetables in the foreground. Under high magnification this contrast is even more clearly visible. In the figures, the relatively thin flesh tones are applied over a grey underpainting, which is left partially exposed to form the shadows; the birds' heads, on the other hand, are modelled by the application of strongly impastoed white highlights.

Preparatory sketches by Rubens for some of these joint works survive, indicating that the designs followed by his fellow collaborators often originated in his studio. Consequently the collaborating artist's contribution was usually added after the figures had been painted in by Rubens (Robels 1989). However close examination of *The Poulterer's Shop* shows that the still-life was applied to the canvas before the painting of the figures. This can be seen from the way the maid's red skirt has been painted around the feet of the heron, and from the pentiment of the cauliflower leaves, which is visible under her sleeve now that the upper paint layer has aged and become more transparent. A similar composition belonging to Lady Bute entitled *Scullery with Maid and Serving Boy,* dating from the mid 1630s, is another example of collaboration where Snyders painted his still-life

An X-radiograph of *The Poulterer's Shop*, showing a dead deer hung by one leg

A detail from *The Poulterer's Shop*

before the figures were inserted by Rubens (Robels 1989).

In normal light an unusual pentiment was observed in the background of *The Poulterer's Shop* at the centre top of the composition alongside the sausages. A full X-radiographic image of the painting was taken to determine what lay beneath the surface paint. The X-ray examination clearly showed that the pentiment formed part of a slaughtered deer hung up by one leg.

During initial visual examination of *The Poulterer's Shop* it was noticed that wherever a lump was present in the ground and the overlying paint layers were worn down, several paint layers were

visible that seemed unrelated to the present image. A paint sample taken from the maid's hand showed three paint layers overlying the original white ground. Taken together with the evidence from the X-ray image, they can now be interpreted as the yellow-brown paint from the earlier image of the hanging deer, followed by a grey priming and finally the pink of the flesh tone in the present image.

The X-ray clearly demonstrates that the additional strip of canvas at the right hand side was present from the outset and is not a later extension, as the deer's head extends into this section of the

A detail from where the sample was taken

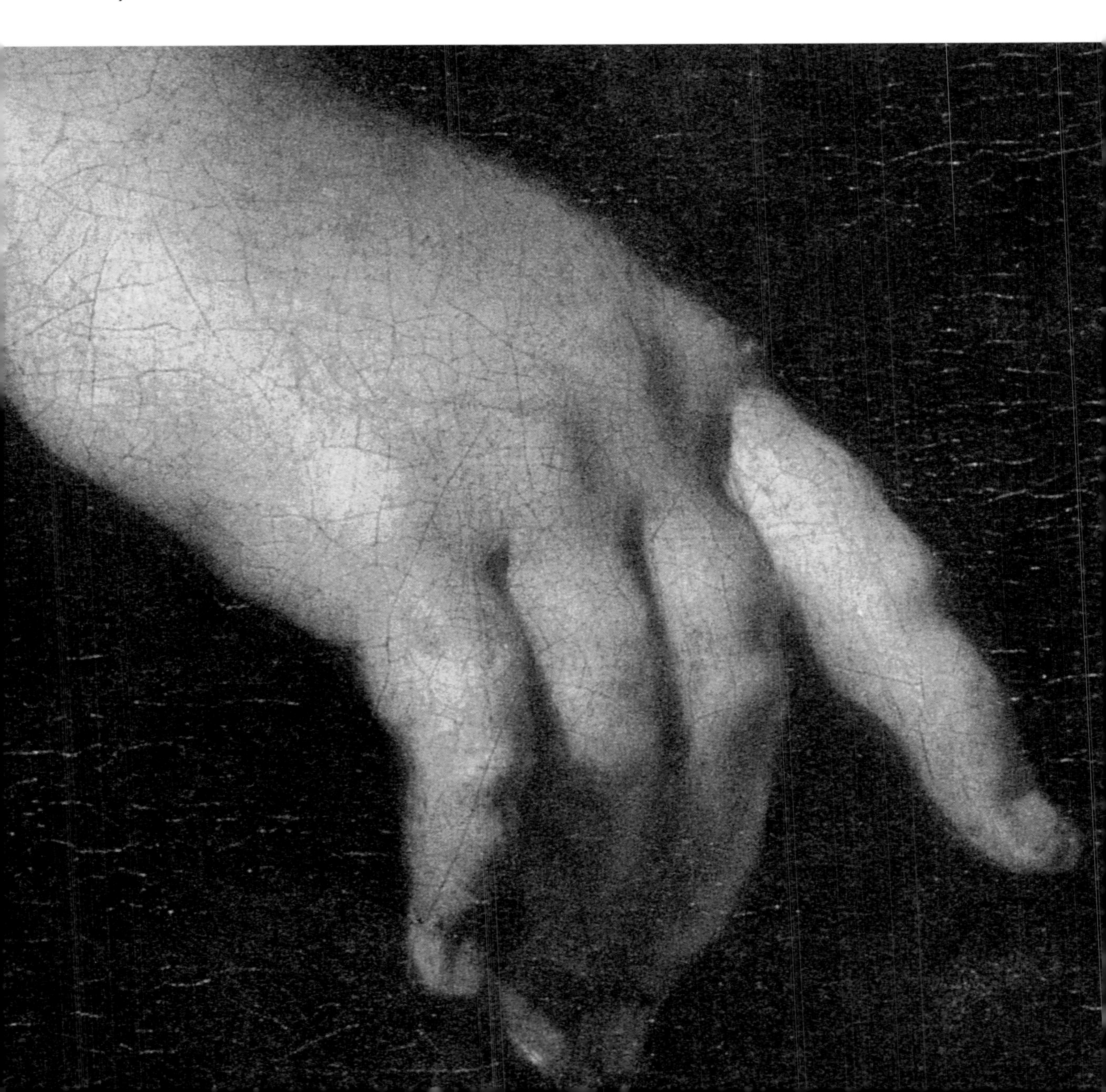

A paint sample cross-section taken from the maid's hand, showing three paint layers overlying the original white ground

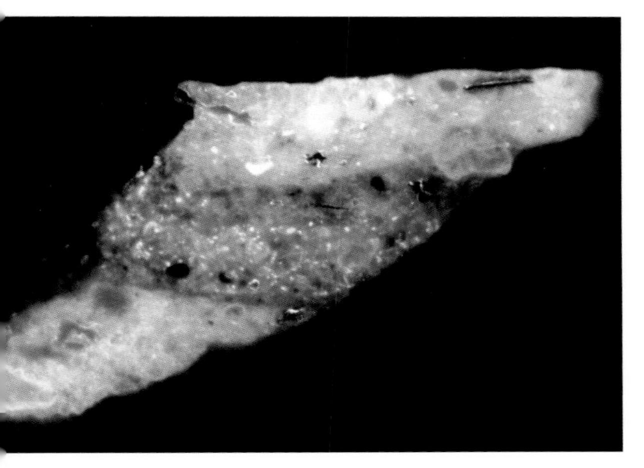

Frans Snyders, *Still-life with Deer, Lobster, Fruit and Vegetables* (Musées Royaux des Beaux Arts de Belgique, Brussels, inv. No. 4951)

support. The diagonal white marks visible in the X-ray image suggests that the original ground layer, which consists largely of coarse chalk with some addition of lead white, was applied or scraped down with a knife.

The underlying composition is recognizable as one of Snyders own works, which is known in several other versions, datable to around 1610, a period when he was specializing in paintings of wild game without the inclusion of figures (Robels 1989). The closest in appearance to our X-radiograph image is the work entitled *Still-life with Deer, Lobster, Fruit and Vegetables* in the Musées Royaux des Beaux-Arts de Belgique, Brussels.

The Brussels painting is signed 'F. Snyders fecit' at the lower right and measures 1,720 x 1,160 mm. It is therefore slightly smaller than *The Poulterer's Shop*, which measures 1,881 x 1,520 mm. The discovery of the underlying painting adds further weight to the attribution of the still-life element of the present painting to Snyders. It also indicates that *The Poulterer's Shop* must have been painted

The Poulterer's Shop,
after cleaning

after 1610 and prior to about 1620, if the attribution of the figures to Arnout Vinckenborch (active 1590-1620) is correct. Most importantly of all, we now know that this painting originated in Snyders' studio and was completed in Rubens' workshop.

Kate Lowry and Rachel Turnbull

VLIEGHE, H. 1987. Rubens' beginnende invloed: Arnout Vinckenborch en het problem van Jordaens' vroeste tekeningen. *Nederlands Kunsthistorisch Jaarboek*, 38.

ROBELS, H. 1989. *Frans Snyders: Stilleben- und Tiermaler, 1579-1657*. Deutscher Kunstverlag, Munich.

The structure of a painting

Most oil paintings are painted on a support of woven canvas (usually a plain weave linen), wood panels or occasionally metal sheet. The support is normally prepared by applying a ground layer, often of chalk bound in animal glue (gesso) or lead white pigment bound in a drying oil. The ground layer provides a smooth, bland, non-absorbent surface to receive the oil paint layer. Oil paints are coloured pigments mixed with a drying oil medium such as linseed or poppy oil. The pigments may be derived from an organic or inorganic source, for example, red earths from naturally occurring clays or carmine red lake from dried beetles.

The paint mixture is diluted with turpentine or white spirit so that it can be applied to the prepared support. The drying oils absorb oxygen and become hard. To protect the paint later and to give it brightness and gloss, a varnish layer is finally applied. Traditionally this is a natural resin such as dammar or mastic dissolved in a solvent, applied on top of the final paint layer to saturate the colours and give a clear transparent coating. In modern paintings and those that have recently been restored, synthetic paints and varnishes are normally used. Natural resins become yellow with age due to oxidation, and often have to be cleaned off and replaced.

Paintings on canvas are supported on a wooden stretcher, which is a wooden frame that can be tensioned out with wooden keys. Tacking margins are the edges of the canvas support that are turned over the sides of the stretcher where the canvas can be attached, usually with metal tacks. The picture is finally mounted in a frame.

Is half a pot a whole object?
Restoration of a Bronze Age Beaker

'Beaker' is a term used to describe a particular type of ceramic vessel dating from the later Neolithic to the Early Bronze Age, and the 'Beaker period' is synonymous with a change in cultural phenomena seen across northern Europe at this time (2500 BC-1700 BC) including a move away from communal burial mounds towards individual interments accompanied by high status grave goods.
Beakers first appear in Britain in megalithic tombs, but are most commonly associated with individual burials in barrows or cists (stone lined burials).

The Beaker in 1919

They were possibly used as drinking vessels or for ceremonial purposes and they were produced in a variety of styles and sizes and with considerable variation in the quality of workmanship. Often they were deposited as complete vessels, but there is also evidence that Beakers were sometimes deliberately broken and stacked, or that even just a single broken sherd was left in a grave (Woodward 2002). It is therefore important with such artefacts that their context and information about their deposition is also investigated. It is likely that Beakers underwent complex symbolic use and therefore should be seen as a more multifaceted phenomenon than simply deposited grave goods.

Several Beaker burials were discovered at Merthyr Mawr in south Wales when a large tumulus that had appeared out of drifting sand dunes was excavated at the beginning of the twentieth century. Two cists were found along with three secondary burials, which all contained individual crouched adults with Beakers (Ward 1919). These Beakers are typical examples of Early Bronze Age ceramics from Wales.

Bronze Age pots were handmade by building up coils of clay onto a base and smoothing over these to create the walls of the vessel. They were decorated with incised lines and patterns, sometimes using cord, shells or bone combs, then probably burnished with a smooth stone and fired in bonfires or pits (Gibson 2002). The firings could reach temperatures of 650°-900°C, but only for short times, and therefore the resulting ceramic often had a hard crust but a soft, crumbly hygroscopic centre (Smith 1998). Even so, Beaker makers often produced very high quality pots.

Museum artefacts often have a history of their own in terms of their conservation. Archaeological knowledge, fashions and display techniques have altered hugely over the last century, and this is often reflected in how objects have been conserved or restored. There is also an issue as to how historically important the restoration itself is, and in what context a modern curator might want to interpret objects from historical excavations. Is it better for an object such as this to represent a complete pot, or is it more important to show its state when buried – bearing in mind that neither will give a complete view of what the ceramic was like or might have originally been used for? One of the Beakers from the Merthyr Mawr tumulus that has been in the Museum for many years was brought to the conservation laboratories, and illustrates many of these issues.

The Beaker has a buff-orange surface and a black core (Savory 1980). It is 172 mm tall with a diameter of 127 mm at the mouth, and the walls of the vessel are on average 6-8 mm thick. Slight residual contours from the coil manufacturing process can be seen on the inner surface; the outer surface is burnished and there is comb incised and bar-chevron decoration on the neck and body of the pot.

The Beaker consisted of nineteen reconstructed sherds, plus a large amount of restoration work that had returned the pot to a complete vessel. (Although there are no records, it is likely that this restoration

Harry Gear in his workshop in the 1960s

The restored beaker, before the recent conservation work

A detail of inside the beaker

work was carried out by a technician called Harry Gear, who worked in the Museum for over fifty years.) The earlier reconstruction was largely undertaken using plaster of Paris, but also contained brick dust and was consolidated and adhered with both shellac and animal glue; the restored areas were coloured using oil paints. Although superficially the gap-filled areas appeared to be in good condition, the restoration and over-painting meant that the condition of the underlying pot, as well as the number of joins, was unknown. When studied more closely, it became clear that much of the fabric of the pot was obscured by the restoration and that the heaviness of the plaster infill was putting the object at risk; cracks were appearing between the pot and the plaster, and this was possibly causing further unseen internal stresses. In addition, the rim and inner surfaces were ingrained with dirt and dust.

Various small areas, especially the edges of the sherds, had been lost during burial; but more significantly, about a third of the whole pot was missing from one side. This appeared to have been detached by a deliberate, slicing blow. It is not known whether the remaining sherds broke in antiquity as a result of this action, as not everything was recorded during excavation. It seems very unlikely, however, that the large missing fragment was lost in the archaeological process; it is more likely that the deposition of half a pot was an intentional, symbolic act.

The substantial and unsubtle reconstruction of the large missing area of the Beaker was the principal issue of concern in respect to its conservation. Both the conservator and curator felt that not only was the restoration potentially damaging the ceramic fabric, but in ethical terms a more 'honest' approach to restoration was required, questioning the need to hide breaks and losses, and especially the need to fill the larger and possibly deliberately made area of loss. After removal, the weight of the plaster infill from this area was found to be approximately one-and-a-half times that of the Beaker itself.

After the plaster had been taken off, cleaning was carried out to identify and expose all the joins and to remove brick dust and any remaining plaster; this was done using a scalpel, acetone swabs and dampened swabs of distilled water. Unfortunately, some of the oil paint applied directly onto the inside surface of the pot had soaked in and left small, patchy stains. During cleaning it became apparent that the whole pot was less stable than initially thought, and two groups of sherds came away completely.

At this point we considered taking down the

An FTIR spectrum of known samples of animal glue (green) and adhesive (black) used on the beaker

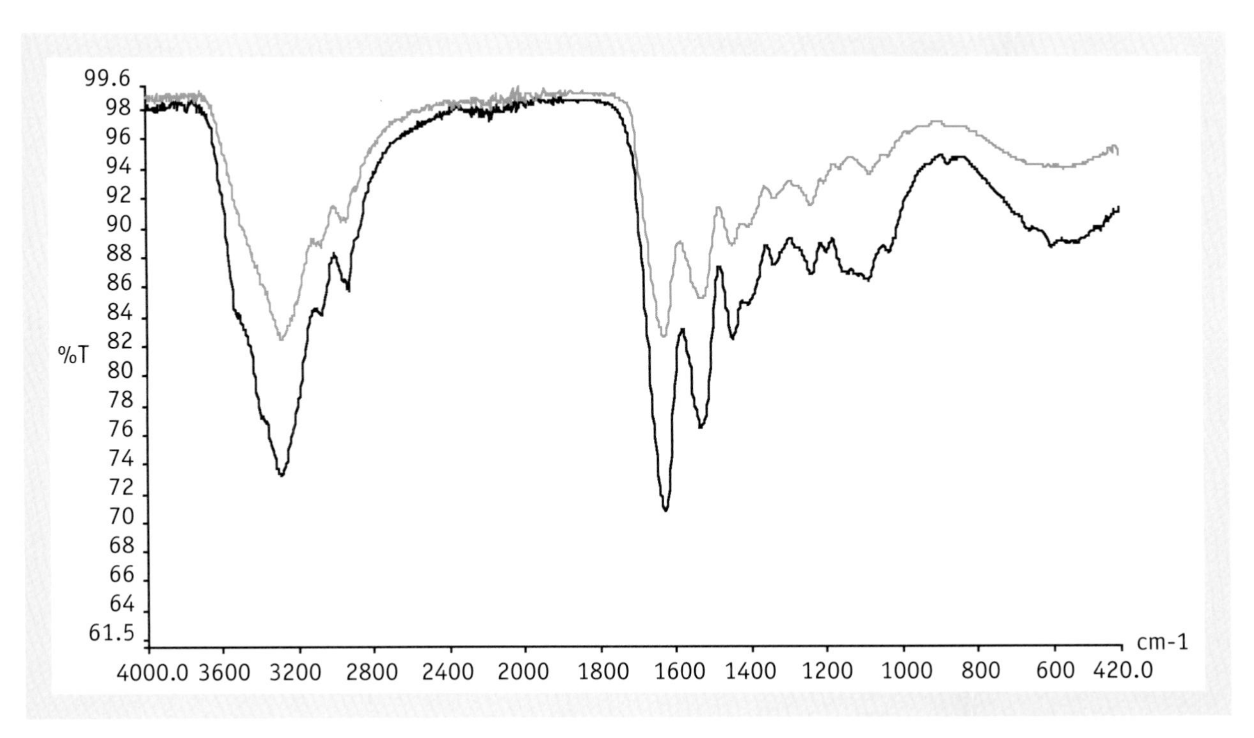

whole pot to its constituent sherds and reassembling the vessel using modern conservation grade materials. FTIR confirmed that both shellac and animal glue were present, but further testing showed that the majority of the fragments had originally been joined with animal glue, with a relatively superficial layer of shellac overlying this. Although the shellac could be removed with IMS, the main joins presented more of a problem.

The best solvent for swelling and removing animal glue is hot water; however, many areas of the low-fired ceramic itself were partially soluble in water and so would have been softened and distorted when wetted. Other methods of removing the animal glue, such as different solvents, dry mechanical cleaning, localised steam humidification and pre-treatment consolidation, could also potentially damage the object. Furthermore, the animal glue had formed a strong physical bond with the ceramic. The joins were robust, both individually and as parts of the whole pot.

These factors led us to believe that dismantling the animal glue joins could damage the ceramic. Many, though not all of the joins had been well-aligned, as the original reconstruction had been undertaken very carefully despite distortions in the shape of the low-fired ceramic – which had probably been caused by burial over hundreds of years in a

The conserved Beaker

damp environment. We therefore decided not to take down the majority of the joins.

The outer surface of the reconstructed sherds of the pot looked good, but the appearance of the inside was unacceptable. Here, hot water was used to remove excess adhesive without compromising the pot's structural strength. Small, vulnerable areas of the pot were consolidated locally under the microscope. Excess animal glue was then removed by applying water on a swab; this was left for a few minutes until the glue had swollen and could easily be scraped away; often several applications were necessary to clear the full thickness of glue. The process was time consuming, as the surrounding fabric softened to a wet biscuit consistency almost immediately when wetted. Further consolidation on other areas of the pot was carried out to strengthen existing hairline cracks. The edges of detached sherds were also treated in this manner before they were re-adhered into place.

The issue of how far to undertake the restoration of the pot was then considered. Some gap fill, although minor, was necessary if the pot was to be displayed upright. For example, some of the inner surface joins needed a small amount of filling for strength, and in the same manner, missing areas of the pot at its waist and front also needed partially filling for structural support. These areas were treated using an adhesive solution with glass balloons; the gap-fill was applied so that it remained 1-2 mm below the surface of the original ceramic, and was then painted so that the reconstructed area could be seen when examined closely, but would blend in from a distance.

The large, intentional area of loss did not require gap-filling for purposes of stability, and a partial pot was felt to represent the use of the vessel at the time of burial: the time in the history of the pot for which we had most archaeological information.

The display of this vessel in a stable but incomplete state helps illustrate the complexity of the archaeological evidence, and how current research in curatorial as well as conservation work alters our perceptions of what should be displayed and how. This can lead to a division in opinion as to what is important in display terms: this object could be seen as a fine piece of early ceramic technology,

The conserved Beaker photographed under ultraviolet light. The fluorescing white inlay in the incised decoration is made from burnt bone; this had not been noticed when examined under visible light, but provides further evidence on how the pot would have looked

an object of artistic worth, a fragment of evidence about past rituals and burial practices and a repository of future information. Organic residues are being extracted from early ceramics that help identify what they contained; further work can enable some of these residues to be radiocarbon dated. Future scientific research might contribute to our knowledge and understanding in unforeseen ways, and there is an obligation on museums not only to make objects in their care accessible through display, but also to preserve as much of the original object in as stable and unaltered state as possible for the future.

Mary Davis and Felicity Woor

CLARKE, D. L. 1970. *Beaker Pottery of Great Britain and Ireland*, Vol. 2. Cambridge University Press, London

GIBSON, A. 2002. *Prehistoric Pottery*. Tempus Publishing, Stroud.

SMITH, S. 1998. British Bronze Age Pottery; an Overview of Deterioration and Current Techniques of Conservation at the British Museum. *The Conservator*, 22, 3-11.

WARD, J. 1919. Prehistoric Burials, Merthyr Mawr Warren, Glamorgan. *Archaeologia Cambrensis*, XIX, 323-352.

WOODWARD, A. 2002. Beads and Beakers: Heirlooms and Relics in the British Early Bronze Age. *Antiquity*, 76, 1040.

The graph below shows two spectral lines taken from identical polypropylene lids. However, one lid (represented by the blue line) has been exposed to light and solvents during use. The arrowed peak shows the formation of carbonyl bonds (C=O), which have weakened the structure of the polypropylene, causing the lid to become brittle and split

Fourier-Transform Infrared Spectrometry (FTIR)

Infrared spectrometry is primarily used for the qualitative analysis of organic materials, for example coatings, varnishes, dyes, fibres and resins.

Infrared spectrometry works by measuring the absorption of infrared radiation by a sample. Infrared radiation is absorbed by atoms vibrating in a molecule; the wavelength absorbed is dependent on the mass of the atoms present, the type of interatomic bond and the neighbouring bonds. Spectra produced do not provide precise chemical characterisation of a sample, but are compared with those of known substances.

The FTIR uses an 'interferometer' to generate infrared radiation of different wavelengths, and by employing a combination of moving and stationary mirrors and a computer to perform complex mathematical (Fourier) analysis, a spectrum of absorbency versus wavelength is produced.

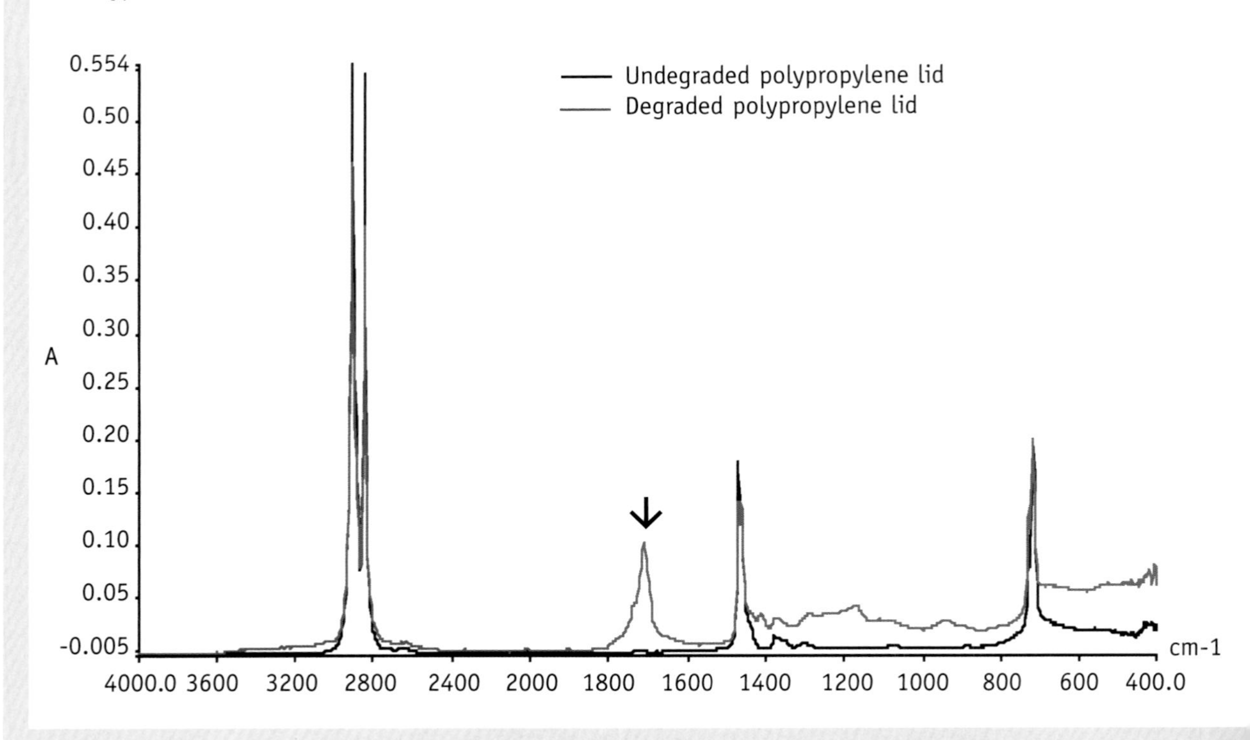

The graph below illustrates the use of FTIR to identify an unknown material. A sample of the substance to be tested was removed from the surface of a piece of fossil bone. The sample was then analysed using the FTIR spectrometer. The resulting spectrum was then compared with a library of known FTIR spectra on a computer and successfully identified as cellulose nitrate

Identification of organic materials is an important curatorial requirement for researching and cataloguing museum collections.
The identification of materials such as plastics, dyes and fibres enhances understanding of the materials but also imparts information about the type and degree of degradation that can occur – even to modern, apparently stable materials such as plastics.

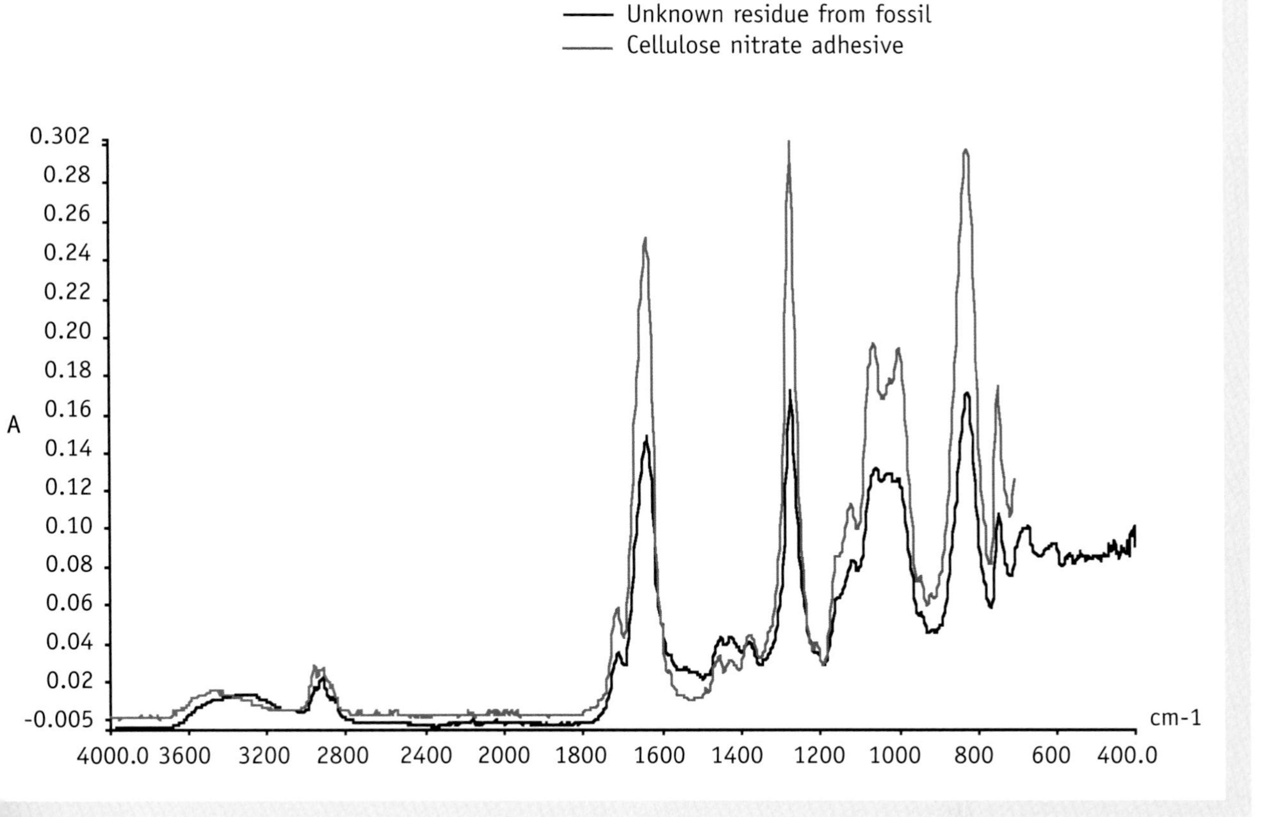

Will it run? Should it run?

Restoring a Benz car

In 1921 the National Museum of Wales took possession of a 1900 Benz 'Duc'. The car had originally been donated to the Science Museum in London in 1911, by a Doctor Cropper from Chepstow; however, as that museum already had a similar and slightly older example in their collection, in 1913 it was offered to the National Museum of Wales. There was then a delay of eight years before it was taken to Cardiff.

The 'Duc' was built by the Benz Motor Company in Mannheim, Germany, and is believed to be one of only two known surviving models of its type. It was built with an 1800cc single cylinder horizontal motor with a transverse shaft located at the rear. The motor runs at 800rpm and produces seven horsepower. The car has the appearance of a carriage with a large enveloping hood, and when this is up the wind resistance is so strong that it severely hampers the progress of the vehicle. The frame is built up of compound wood and iron and iron side members and the wheels are wood with solid rubber tyres.

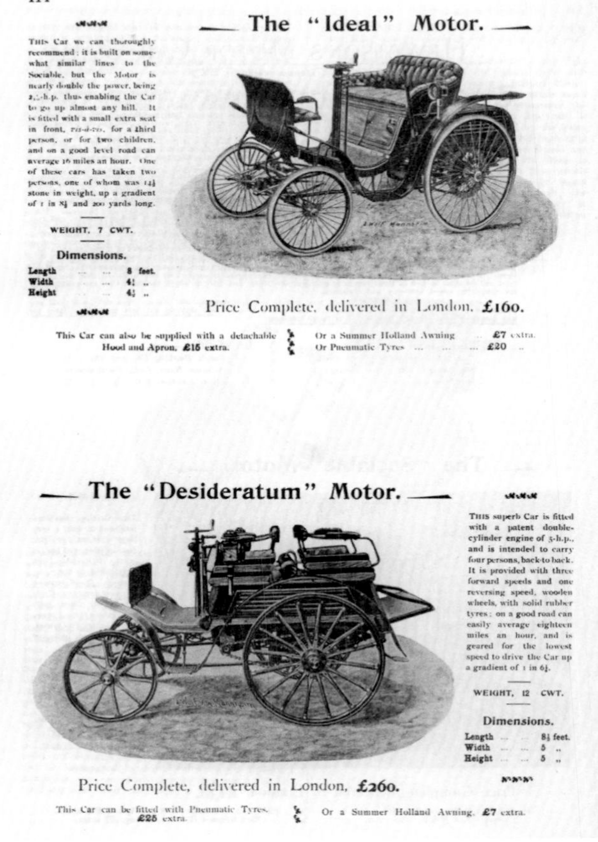

114

The "Ideal" Motor.

This Car we can thoroughly recommend; it is built on somewhat similar lines to the Sociable, but the Motor is nearly double the power, being 2¾-h.p. thus enabling the Car to go up almost any hill. It is fitted with a small extra seat in front, *vis-à-vis*, for a third person, or for two children, and on a good level road can average 16 miles an hour. One of these cars has taken two persons, one of whom was 14½ stone in weight, up a gradient of 1 in 8½ and 200 yards long.

WEIGHT, 7 CWT.

Dimensions.

Length	8 feet.
Width	4½ „
Height	4½ „

Price Complete, delivered in London. **£160.**

This Car can also be supplied with a detachable Hood and Apron, **£15** extra. Or a Summer Holland Awning ... **£7** extra. Or Pneumatic Tyres ... ... **£20** „

The "Desideratum" Motor.

This superb Car is fitted with a patent double-cylinder engine of 5-h.p., and is intended to carry four persons, back-to-back. It is provided with three forward speeds and one reversing speed, wooden wheels, with solid rubber tyres; on a good road can easily average eighteen miles an hour, and is geared for the lowest speed to drive the Car up a gradient of 1 in 6½.

WEIGHT, 12 CWT.

Dimensions.

Length	8½ feet.
Width	5 „
Height	5 „

Price Complete, delivered in London, **£260.**

This Car can be fitted with Pneumatic Tyres, **£25** extra. Or a Summer Holland Awning, **£7** extra.

Left: original advertisements for Benz cars

Below: the car, before conservation

When the car returned to Wales it was kept in a barn at St Fagans, at the mercy of the elements. It was then moved to the National Museum Cardiff, to take up residence in a warm, dry basement for a number of years. Although this was good storage for the engine metalwork, the leather components of the hood became increasingly desiccated and degraded. It survived suggestions in the 1960s that, due to the fact it had never been exhibited and because of a lack of space, the car should be disposed of.

In 1977 the Welsh Industrial & Maritime Museum was opened, and the Benz motor car was moved to this site in Cardiff Bay. It was then that curatorial and conservation interest in the car and its display provided the opportunity to address the future of this vehicle within a museum context, and in doing so raise the profile of the industrial exhibits. It was decided to try and restore the car to working order with a view to entering it in the annual London to Brighton Veteran Car Rally (which is open to cars manufactured before December 31 1904). This would, in effect, exhibit the car to hundreds of thousands of people, and increase the profile of the National Museum of Wales.

The restoration of motorcars presents various ethical and procedural dilemmas, but the Benz 'Duc' is rare and very unusual and was to prove more challenging than most.

There has been much argument about the desirability of restoration as opposed to conservation. The general trend nowadays is toward conserving rather than restoring, but with historical working machinery the ethical debate is more complex. Unique items in original condition should be, perhaps, conserved unaltered, whereas objects that were produced in relatively large numbers and still exist in various conditions can lend themselves

to alternative interpretations (Meehan 2000). The restoration of veteran cars to working condition must be considered in a different way from restoring a non-functioning vehicle. Worn or missing parts have to be replaced and all machinery must comply with modern health and safety standards (Newey 2000). The restoration must result in a recreation of the vehicle, not a pastiche (Child 1993).

The initial aim of the project was to attempt to get the car into a roadworthy condition and to run

The restored engine

it, without compromising it as an original artefact, and to this end work was concentrated on the engine. First, a thorough examination was undertaken to ascertain the condition of the whole car and what, if anything, was missing. Many hours were spent examining all components in order to determine how much wear and tear was acceptable. Not only was it necessary to understand the mechanics of the car, but it was also necessary to work out how the car was actually driven.

There are many references on the subject of veteran cars that give information about ignition systems, carburettors, engine set-ups and the like, such as *The Restoration of Vintage and Thoroughbred Cars* by Richard C. Wheatley and Brian Morgan (1969). Advice was also sought from the Veteran Car Club and its members, all of whom were very willing to offer help.

The car had lain idle for over seventy years and so the first task was to consider the feasibility of it running again. All relevant parts were examined thoroughly, including crack testing by spraying on crack-revealing dye. Apart from piston rings 'gummed up' from oxidation of the lubricating oil, a missing drive belt and numerous leaks in the cooling system, the motor looked sound. The only major part that had to be replaced was the annular brass condenser, which had stress corrosion exacerbated by having been cleaned with an ammonium-based product, so we made a new condenser. All original parts that had to be replaced were kept and stored for reference.

The motor was carefully reassembled and lubricated. The original leather drive belts were missing and were replaced with three-layered belts of leather with an inner layer of Kevlar™. These gave the friction of leather, but did not stretch like the originals.

With the engine back in position, the ignition system was examined. This is a relatively simple affair, using a 'trembler' ignition coil and a battery. The original ignition coil had burnt out and was replaced with a new one, housed in the original casing. The system does not have a generator, which means the battery is discharging as the motor is running and so has to be recharged periodically, and this is now done using a modern portable battery charger.

Once the engine was restored, the settings had to be investigated. For example, at what point should the ignition be set? What should the fuel level be in the carburettor? How rich should the air-fuel mixture be? Although the starting point here is sound theoretical knowledge, in practice several series of minor adjustments, gained from experience using different settings, are tried until an optimum is reached for that particular engine.

To make the car safe to use and certified as roadworthy, the brakes, steering and transmission had to be inspected, and where necessary worn parts were repaired or replaced ready for its MOT test (an MOT edict states that when testing veteran cars, they have to be of the standard applicable when they were designed). To ensure safe driving on the road, we made new steel pins and phosphor bronze bushes to replace all the old ones. The car passed the test, despite having no lights, indicators or wiper blades. The car runs on motor spirit, a petroleum product similar to lighter fuel, which is obtained locally from a specialist factory.

Once the engine was working, the next step was to learn how to drive the car. First, the back was raised up and all the levers and mechanisms were examined to understand the effect of each lever in turn. When the functions of the driving mechanisms were understood, a test drive was carried out on a private road owned by the Docks Board, alongside the foreshore in Cardiff. This road was deserted, a mile long, dead straight and perfect for a test site. The car was taken there on a trailer and, with the van and trailer in close attendance, the car was driven properly for the first time in over seventy years. As time went on, the car became easier to start and ran more smoothly; a combination of familiarity and minor adjustments steadily helped improve its running mechanisms.

During the restoration of the engine, work on the body of the car was kept to a minimum. The woodwork, most of which is still original (except for part of a floorboard, the tool box cover and a small panel at the rear), was cleaned and coated with linseed oil. The metalwork was also cleaned, the rust removed where necessary and a protective coating of linseed oil applied. Corrosion and rust were not always removed from metal components, as in some cases they formed a degree of protection to the underlying metal which would corrode again at a faster rate if stripped bare. The tyres are solid; although Benz did try pneumatic tyres on this model,

The leather cushions and trim before restoration

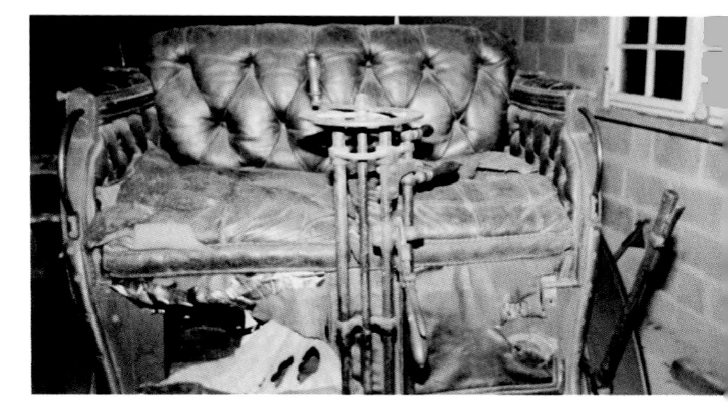

they caused too much trouble and so he reverted to solid ones. Owing to their poor condition these needed replacing, but similar traditional carriage tyres are still produced today.

The car now regularly takes part in the London to Brighton Veteran Car Rally. The run itself is more of an endurance test for the driver than the car. Seven hours or so, tightly clutching the steering tiller while concentrating on the road, and with winds and draughts blowing all around, gives the driver and passengers a very real sense of what driving was like at the turn of the twentieth century.

After a few years of running in its original condition, it became apparent that the hood and the leather cushions and trim, which had suffered dreadful damage from the storage conditions endured between 1922 and 1977, would have to be replaced. This decision was not taken lightly, but the trim was very fragile and becoming irreparably damaged with use. A number of specialist coach trimmers were contacted with the brief to use the same materials and techniques as the original. The chosen contractor worked closely with us to ensure an authentic replica was produced. The danger with

The leather cushions and trim, being restored

partly restoring an object is the restored areas can exaggerate the untidiness of the rest. Thus, if the trim is attended to, the paintwork will then look untidy, and so on until everything has been replaced. In the case of the Benz, the original paint finish has been retained, so although there is some discrepancy in its overall appearance, the car still looks its age.

During the years the car has been running, more has been learnt about how it actually works and the problems faced by Carl Benz in manufacturing such an early model; this type of information about the object could not have been obtained from a static exhibit. For instance, the steering mechanism used on this car needed to be modified from that used for a horse-drawn coach, as the inside wheels turn in more sharply and move less when rounding a corner. When a machine is a static exhibit in a gallery only the eyes are engaged, but when it is running other senses are involved: the vibrations can be felt, the engine heard and the fuel and oil smelled. It also becomes a much more accessible object, seen within its context on the roads and by a much wider audience than would make a trip to visit it in a gallery or in store.

The curators and conservators working on this project felt certain that by running the car and maintaining the engine in working order, the display life and potential of the car were being used far more effectively than leaving the engine rusted and seized up. It partly seemed a question of either slowly wearing out the parts in use, or neglecting them within a static display until they are likely never to become functional again. Neither may be an ideal outcome, but there is always an element of compromise with preserving and displaying complex, vulnerable materials if they are also to remain part of a public, accessible collection.

Chris Perry

BALL, S. & WINSOR, P. 1997. *Larger and Working Objects*. Museums & Galleries Commission, London.

CHILD, R. E. 1993. Restoration and Conservation: Ethic, 297-302. In FLEMING, D., PAINE, C. & RHODES. J. G. (eds). *Social History in Museums – a Handbook for Professionals*. HMSO, London.

MEEHAN, P. M. 2000. *Is Reversibility an Option when Conserving Industrial Collections?* 11-17. In ODDY, A. & CARROLL, S. (eds). *Reversibility – does it exist?* British Museum Occasional Paper No.135, London.

NEWEY, H. 2000. Conservation and the Preservation of Scientific and Industrial Collections. 137-139. In ROY, A. & SMITH, P (eds). *Traditions and Innovations*. IIC Congress, Melbourne.

The car, after conservation

'but little disturbance of the bones...' Conserving a fossil sea reptile

The recording and conservation of museum objects is often routine work. It is, therefore, exciting when treatments reveal new, unexpected information about a specimen. This may happen with recent acquisitions, but also sometimes with specimens that have been in a collection for over a century.

Routine monitoring of the palaeontological collections in the Department of Geology identified an ichthyosaur specimen which was damaged and needed remedial work to stabilise it and prevent fragmented pieces from becoming dislodged and lost. What was envisaged as a relatively straightforward job turned into a major conservation project, which revealed new information about the nature and preparation of the specimen.

Ichthyosaurs were marine reptiles that lived in the oceans at the time when dinosaurs occupied the land, from 220 million years to 65 million years ago (Howe et al. 1981). They had an appearance similar to that of dolphins, with distinctive long jaws, sharp teeth and large eyes.

Ichthyosaurs have been recognized for over 300 years, and they were first interpreted as fish, lizards and even sea dragons. The nineteenth century witnessed a huge increase in the public's fascination with geology and the living world. New museums were established with natural history collections and exhibits, and ichthyosaurs were a desirable addition to these collections. Many specimens from this period were mounted in plaster and encased in wooden frames; the plaster was painted to look like rock and then the object was hung on the wall (Cornish et al. 1995).

This damaged specimen, although now housed in the palaeontology store, had previously been on public display for many years. The ichthyosaur, seemingly in rock of Jurassic age, had been donated to the former Cardiff Municipal Museum in the 1880s, not long after its opening. Unfortunately, like many other similar fossils in the collection, it was not numbered, so there is no information regarding its history and provenance. When the National Museum of Wales was established in 1907, the ichthyosaur was incorporated into the collections here.
Recent curatorial research has suggested that it might be from Street in Somerset; the paper label in the corner of the specimen identified it as the species *Ichthyosaurus intermedius* collected from that locality. The label also stated that it was 'the greater part of the skeleton of a small individual preserved

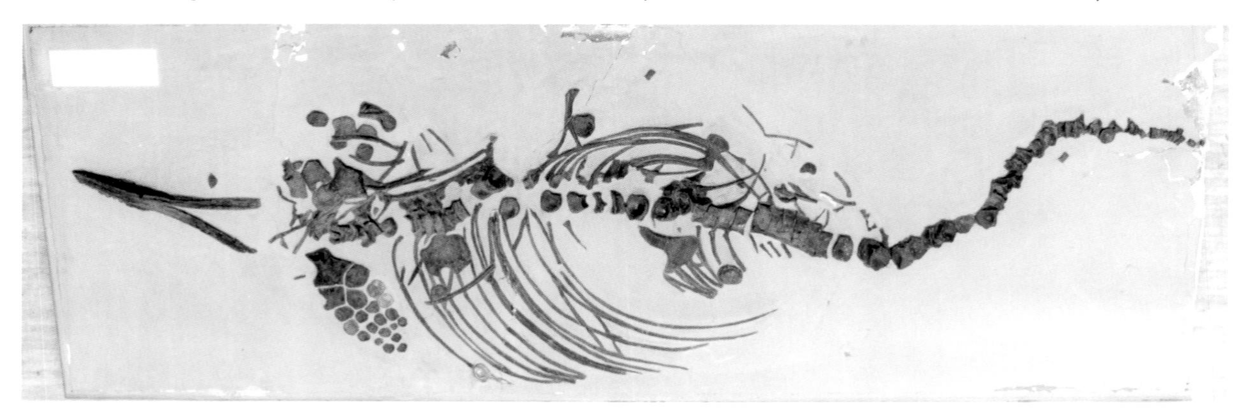

The ichthyosaur specimen, before conservation

The specimen when it was on display at the Museum

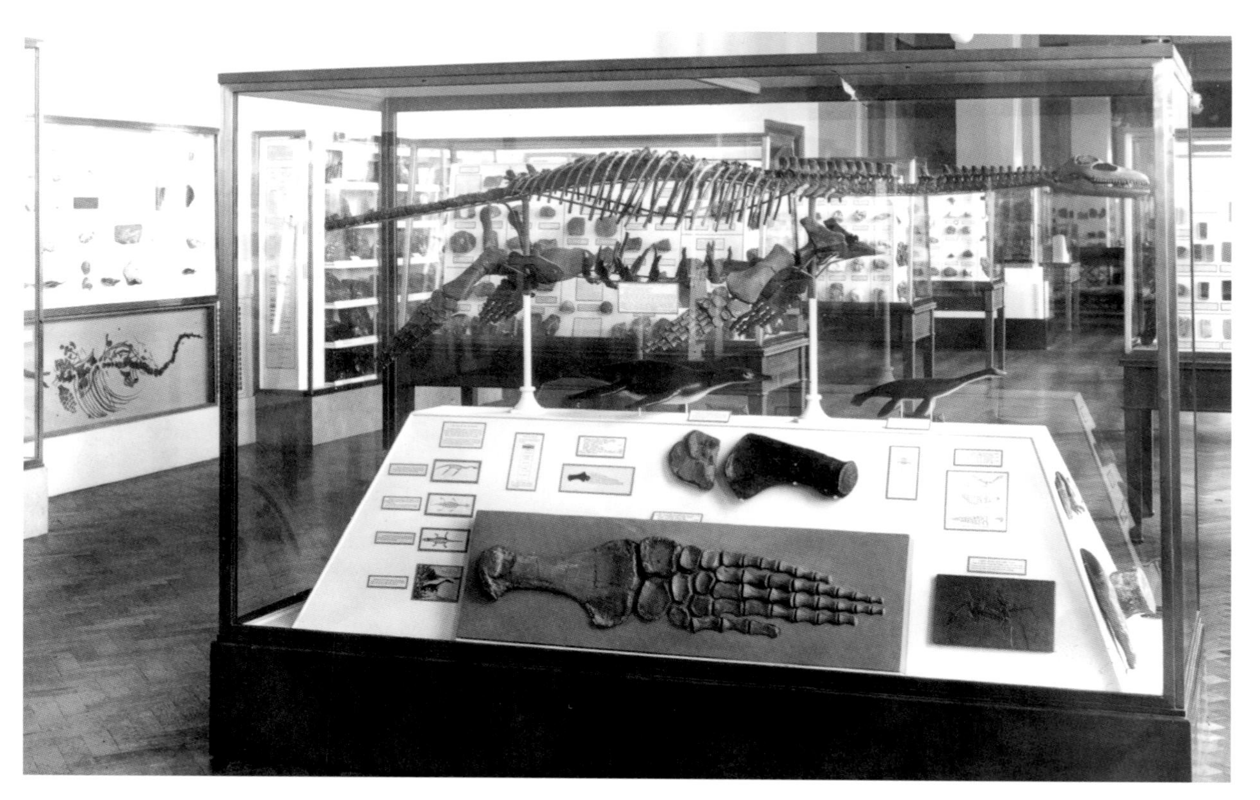

with but little disturbance of the bones' – as the project progressed we realized that this statement was in fact very misleading!

The ichthyosaur specimen is an incomplete skeleton comprising the lower jaw, front paddle, ribs, vertebrae and part of the hind limbs. It had been prepared originally to expose part of the bone in the rock matrix before being set in plaster and surrounded by a wooden frame. The bones had been highlighted using brown paint, and the original rock and surrounding plaster were covered with several layers of grey paint. The frame was very heavy and was made from a base of wooden panels covered with an outer sheet of thin plywood; behind this in the middle of the specimen was one wooden strut perpendicular to the long edges. Iron nails had been used to key the plaster surrounding the specimen to the wooden panels. The specimen showed evidence of having been restored several times during the twentieth century, although no records or information exist about this work. These restorations included the addition of new plaster and repainting.

Major damage to the specimen, due to extensive cracking across its entire width, had caused

Cracked plaster, containing the ichthyosaur bones

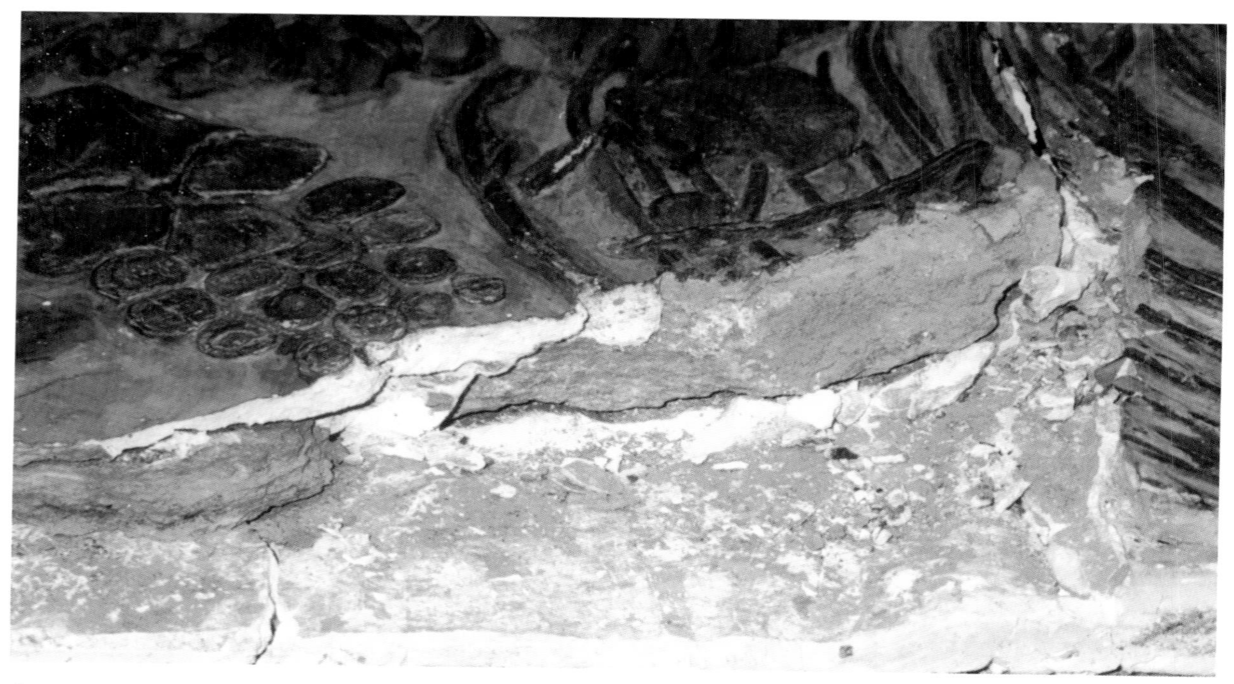

fragments to become dislodged. A tracing was made on transparent sheeting, showing the location of the bones and all the cracks; this came to serve as an invaluable reference map throughout the whole project. The sides of the wooden frame were removed to examine less accessible areas of the specimen more closely. Further damage was revealed, with more large cracks running through both the bones and the surrounding plaster. It became clear that each time the specimen was moved, the wooden support strut underneath the thin baseboard of the frame caused the frame to flex and the plaster and specimen to crack. Areas of the specimen were X-rayed to help identify damage to the bone and rock matrix within the whole specimen.

The purpose of the conservation work at the beginning of the project was to stabilise the specimen so that it could be returned to storage. We hoped that there might be a clear distinction between the original Victorian mount and all subsequent restorations, and that the latter could be removed to reveal the surface as it had been prepared in the nineteenth century. After removing the paint from small test areas we realized that no such differentiation could be made. The entire mount was in such poor condition that we decided to extract the skeleton and rock from the plaster and wooden frame, remove all the paint and remount the ichthyosaur.

While this conservation strategy would remove

An X-ray of the vertebral column, showing areas with plaster fill and repositioned bones

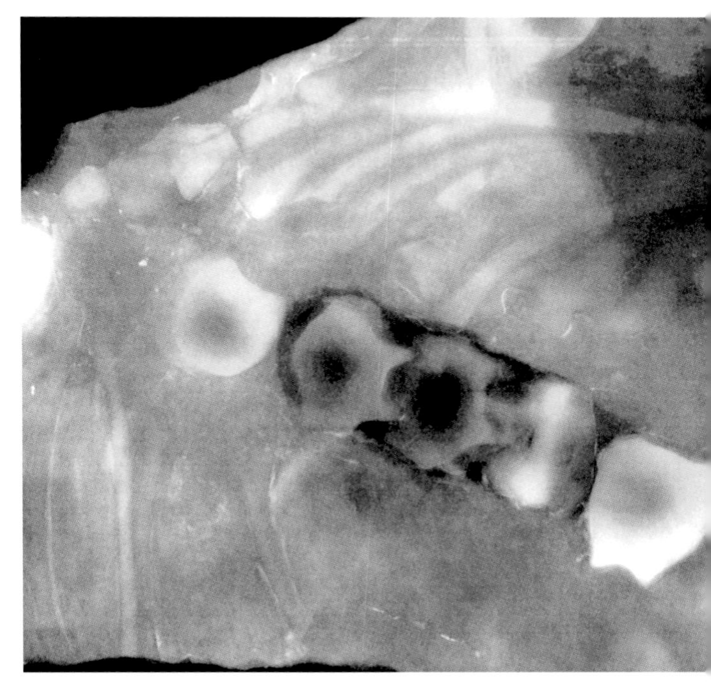

the recent historical context of the specimen and radically alter its appearance, it would allow more to be learnt about the scientific nature of this ichthyosaur and the way it was prepared. To record as much historical information as possible, detailed photographs and diagrams were made of the different paint and plaster layers as they were revealed, and corresponding samples were taken as records.

Conservation work was carried out on the front surface of the ichthyosaur where fragments of bone were cracked and lifting away, and where later restoration work had to be removed. An all-purpose paint remover within a gel was applied to the bones, rock and the surrounding plaster to soften the surface paint, which could then be removed. The surface was then rinsed to remove any residual chemicals. Care was taken during the paint removal to look for any older labels or markings placed on the specimen between the different paint layers, as this is common for fossil vertebrate specimens. None, however, were found.

The skeleton and rock matrix were then excavated from the plaster using a range of instruments such as scalpels and dental tools. The plaster itself contained a variety of fillers, including fragments of rock, brick, glazed tile and a fibrous material. Because it was known that asbestos had been used as a filler in mounted marine reptiles until the 1970s (Cornish et al. 1995), some of these fibres were removed and examined. Fortunately, they turned out to be jute. Samples of all the fill materials were taken for future reference. Small amounts of plaster left adhering to the bone and rock surfaces were removed with an air-abrasive machine. The fossil bones were fragile and so were consolidated by brushing on a conservation grade acrylic (Paraloid B-72™). Small fragments that had become dislodged were reattached using the Paraloid B-72™ as an adhesive.

As the paint was removed and the individual pieces extracted from the plaster, surprising discoveries were made about the true nature of the specimen and about the techniques used by the Victorian preparators.

The rock matrix containing the jaw was of a different colour and lithology to that which contained the rest of the skeleton. This meant that the ichthyosaur skeleton was in fact a composite of at least two separate individuals. Subsequent identification by Dr Chris McGowan, an expert on ichthyosaurs from the Royal Ontario Museum, Canada, revealed that the two individuals were in fact of different species.

The removal of paint layers also revealed that several parts of the ichthyosaur bones were in fact plaster reconstructions. For example, the missing ends of the ribs had been moulded in plaster and then painted to match the rest of the bones, giving the impression that the skeleton was more complete than it actually was.

The X-rays of the ichthyosaur had revealed a dark shadow surrounding the bones in one section of the vertebral column, which was difficult to explain. This was due to a channel that had been cut into the rock matrix, where individual loose vertebrae had been fitted and secured with plaster. This same technique of repositioning bone fragments had also been used in other areas of the specimen. The vertebrae from the channel were removed and cleaned. However, it was impossible to ascertain their original location, so they were returned to the channel and attached using Paraloid B-72™ with glass beads as a filler. Where it was possible to match up (repositioned) bone fragments to their original site, these were extracted and attached correctly with Paraloid B-72™ adhesive. Otherwise, all the remaining pieces were left where the Victorian preparators had placed them.

The bones from the single, seemingly well preserved front paddle of the ichthyosaur turned out to be a composite, made from individually extracted bones that had been rearranged in plaster and cement. In the surrounding rock matrix, holes were found from where individual bones might have been taken before being reconstructed as an undamaged paddle. We decided to retain the 'Victorian' form of the paddle for display purposes, and not to remove the repositioned bones from the plaster and cement.

Before conservation, the ichthyosaur had clearly had a domed upper surface. However, once the

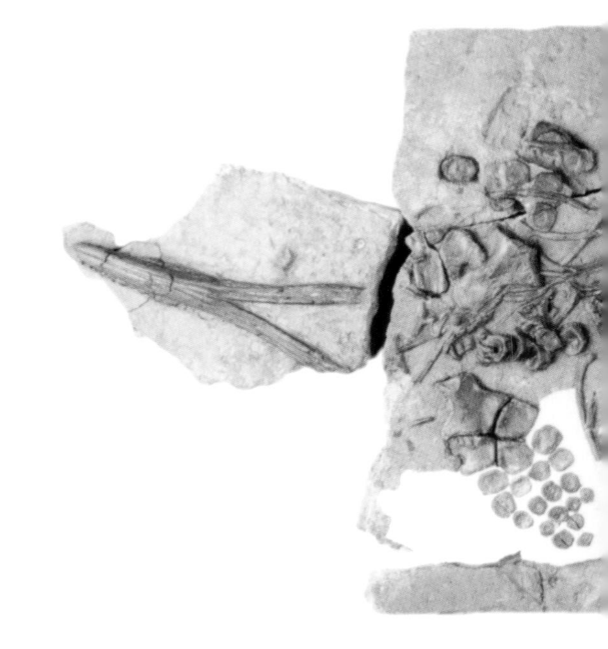

individual parts had been extracted, it could be seen that this shape did not bear any relation to that of the original specimen. The curvature had been primarily due to the way in which the plaster mount had been prepared.

The statement on the label that the specimen was an individual preserved with 'but little disturbance of the bones' was now shown to be untrue. Although some of the Victorian techniques used on the ichthyosaur could have been discovered without such extensive treatment, the full extent of this reconstruction would not have then been revealed. There are previous descriptions of Victorian fossil preparators 'enhancing' vertebrate specimens, probably for financial gain (Cruickshank 1994), and this project gives further insight into

The specimen, after conservation

their techniques.

Once the bone and rock fragments had been extracted from the plaster we had to decide how to remount the ichthyosaur. Although the specimen was made up of two different species, we decided that they should be remounted together as this would make them into a potentially interesting and educational display. This could be used to demonstrate two taxonomic specimens, the work of Victorian preparators and current conservation practice.

The specimen required a rigid, strong, but relatively lightweight cradle support, which would allow it to be stored and transported easily, but would also allow individual pieces to be examined and studied. Traditionally, as with this specimen, fossil marine reptiles have been mounted in plaster in a wooden frame (Cornish et al. 1995). Lightweight alternatives such as fibre-glass supports (Lindsay & Comerford 1996) and epoxy resin are often used these days. For this project, an epoxy resin laminating paste (Epopast™) was chosen. It is a very light, strong support material with the additional advantages of being easy to work with.
It is a fibrous paste with a working time of approximately two hours before it sets solid.

For each piece a small quantity of Epopast™ was shaped by hand to match roughly the outline of the specimen. The specimen was wrapped in a thin polyester film to prevent direct contact and contamination, and was then pressed into the paste, forming a mould of its under-surface. The amount

The conserved specimen on display at the Museum

Press coverage of the discovery

used was adjusted to ensure that the height of adjoining sections matched. When the moulds set, the specimen fragments were removed and unwrapped.

In the central area of the specimen, six pieces fitted together closely, so the individual moulds were joined together. Each mount was then painted to match the colour of the rock or bone fragment.

The individual mounts were then fixed to a rigid base panel of aluminium alloy honeycomb core, faced with a glass fibre filled epoxy skin; this was chosen because it is light but strong and rigid. Using the tracing of the pre-treatment specimen as a guide, the mounts were laid out in their correct positions, and fixed to the panel with an epoxy adhesive. The panel was then painted blue to highlight the specimen. The new mount holds the specimen horizontally and makes the individual fragments accessible for handling and study.

The newly mounted specimen, with an acrylic cover, was put on display in the Glanely Gallery, an interactive hands-on area in the National Museum Cardiff.

The project unexpectedly attracted wide media attention. A press release announced a gallery talk on the conservation of the specimen, which resulted in the story being covered in the national and international press in addition to television, radio, and the internet. Many of the reporters tried to sensationalise the story, without checking all the facts. However, the media coverage did generate a large amount of publicity for geological conservation, and enquiries were received from around the world.

Caroline Buttler

CORNISH, L., DOYLE, A. M. & SWANNELL, J. 1995. The Gallery 30 Project: Conservation of a collection of fossil marine reptiles. *The Conservator*, 19, 20-28.

CRUICKSHANK, A. R. I. 1994. A Victorian fossil wholemount technique: a cautionary tale for our times. *The Geological Curator*, 6, 17-22.

HOWE, S., SHARPE, T. & TORRENS, H. S. 1981. *Ichthyosaurs: a history of fossil 'sea-dragons'.* National Museum of Wales, Cardiff.

LINDSAY, W. & COMERFORD, G. M. 1996. An unusual method of mounting an icthyosaur. *The Geological Curator*, 6, 221-225.

An ammonite deteriorating because of pyrite decay

Pyrite decay

Pyrite decay or sulphide oxidation is arguably the most destructive problem that confronts conservators caring for geological collections. It can result in the total destruction of a specimen.

The decay of the minerals pyrite and marcasite occurs when the sulphide component oxidises to form ferrous sulphate and sulphur dioxide. After further oxidation and hydrolysis a variety of ferrous-ferric-sulphate-hydroxide-hydrate phases are formed. The acid phase produced can attack associated mineral assemblages, resulting in a complex suite of reaction products. The sulphuric acid produced leads to the damage of specimen labels and storage materials. Pyrite decay can be identified by fracturing of specimens, efflorescent decay products, sulphurous smell and acid damage to packaging materials.

Pyrite decay has been recognized for a long time and there is a history of treatments. Earliest methods used involved immersion in fluids to isolate the specimens from the air. There have been a wide variety of treatments that have attempted to neutralise the acidic decay products. Pyrite decay is an electrochemical reaction, but in the 1970s it was considered a bacterial reaction and bactericides were applied to specimens, to no effect.

It is suggested that material at risk should be stored at low humidities: it is recommended that freshly collected, unoxidised pyrite and marcasite specimens should be stored below 30 per cent relative humidity. This could be problematic when pyrite is found finely disseminated through shale, which will delaminate at low humidities. However, anoxic microenvironments are now used to store vulnerable material, which will prevent the oxidation reaction occurring while a suitable level of relative humidity is maintained.

Moulding, casting and replication

Replicas and copies preserve the essentials, so that the essentials can be preserved.

Casts, models and replicas have always played important roles in museums, and especially in conservation. The production of casts enables wider access to rare and fragile material for study, education and display, and sometimes as a primary source of information when unstable objects cannot be preserved in their original state.

Replicas of objects can hold information that would otherwise have been lost. Many casts were taken of early Christian monuments from Wales in the nineteenth century for display in the Museum. These now show more detail than the originals, which have suffered the effects of exposure to the elements for over a century. The casts now have a status as unique records and valued objects in their own right.

Moulding and casting can be used to reconstruct an object; filling in the missing pieces on an incomplete ceramic can indicate the original shape, and can also strengthen the object, enabling display and study. Similarly, dinosaur skeletons are rarely complete, but modelling can make the remains easier to interpret. There are now numerous ways in which this is done, from replicating bones, to life-like models, to the virtual moving images now routinely created for natural history television programmes. Similarly, missing information can be sought through the forensic reconstruction of human skulls, a method increasingly employed by museums to show us how our ancestors looked.

Many museum displays consist of original and replicated material. Both replicas and models are often employed as props to place the main specimens in context. It is also sometimes difficult to move or loan material for exhibitions at different venues; this can be because of the object's condition but also,

occasionally, for political reasons. High quality replicas can then be used as substitutes in displays. Experimental archaeology is another means by which artefacts are replicated, this time using traditional methods and materials, so that ancient technologies can be better understood.

Moulds taken from certain specimens are also an invaluable tool for detailed study and investigation. Examination of the moulds of parts of an object under the SEM can enable fine detail to be studied, such as microscopic tool work on archaeological artefacts, or inaccessible detail within a natural history specimen, for example the inside of a shell or fossil.

In a commercial world replicas can also serve as means of revenue for museums, with posters of works of art and copies of specimens and artefacts for sale. The methods of replication are numerous and becoming evermore sophisticated. Laser scanning and modelling can now produce highly accurate three-dimensional reproductions of complicated objects with no contact to the original, and in a variety of materials ranging from stone to resin.

Nature in glass
The models of Leopold and Rudolf Blaschka

The second half of the nineteenth century was a time of great scientific discovery. Throughout the world, new museums were being built and many private museums were opened to the public. New galleries were designed to display the range of known living plants and animals. For many groups of animals this was easily done. Birds, mammals, reptiles and even fish could be skinned and mounted to produce reasonably accurate and lifelike representations. Insects, with their hard exoskeletons, were dried and pinned to boards for study or display. But what about soft-bodied animals, such as jellyfish and sea anemones, which were preserved in spirit? Their colours quickly faded and their shapes became distorted as the tissues shrank. The German glass-worker and naturalist Leopold Blaschka devised a solution to this problem. Together with his son, Rudolf, he established a successful business supplying glass models, mostly of marine animals, to museums worldwide during the latter half of the nineteenth century.

Leopold Blaschka was born in 1822 at Aicha, in Northern Bohemia, now the Czech Republic. The Blaschka family, originally from Venice, were skilled workers in decorative glass, and Leopold showed artistic skill from an early age. When he left school he spent some time apprenticed as a goldsmith and gemcutter, before joining his father's business crafting ornaments from metal and glass. For many years Leopold continued to produce decorative items and jewellery. Alongside the business, Leopold maintained an interest in natural history. His son Rudolf was born on 17 June 1857, and it was around this time that Leopold began experimenting with making artificial glass flowers. He was introduced to Prince Camille de Rohan, a wealthy amateur naturalist, who arranged to supply Leopold with specimens of orchids from his greenhouses for study. Between 1860 and 1862 Leopold constructed about one hundred models, representing about fifty species of orchids. In the summer of 1863, the models were displayed in the pavilion of the Botanical Garden in Dresden. They attracted a lot of attention for their beauty and craftsmanship, but, although much

Left: Leopold and Rudolf Blaschka (Images courtesy of the Botanical Museum, Harvard University, Cambridge, MA)

Right: an intricate model of a Portugese Man-of-war (*Physalia arethusa*)

admired, no commercial interest was shown in them.

In the same year, an Englishman living in Dresden, whose name was never recorded, asked Leopold to make models of sea-anemones. He provided a copy of a recently published book, *Actinologia Britannica* by P. H. Gosse, for reference. Leopold produced a set of models, which were purchased by Professor Reichenbach for the Dresden Museum. These models, exhibited in artificial aquaria, attracted the attention of curators of the new natural history museums and Leopold began supplying sets of anemones to museums and private collectors across Europe. Inspired by his success with the anemones, he recalled a voyage to America in 1853 when he had spent time observing jellyfish. He remembered being very taken by their glass-like appearance, and soon he had added models of these animals to his repertoire.

In 1870 Rudolf, then a young teenager, began to learn the traditional family skills by assisting in his father's workshop. From 1866 onwards the business only received modest orders for models each year, so they supplemented their income by making decorative items of jewellery, medical glassware and glass eyes, mostly for cosmetic use by blind people but also for taxidermists. In 1876 they received an order for two complete collections of models for the South Kensington Museum in London, now the Natural History Museum. Rudolf was then further inspired to study zoology and anatomy, and made much use of the great natural history library of the Imperial Academy Leopoldina in Dresden. Here the Blaschkas studied illustrated books and copied many of the drawings as sources of reference for the glass animals.

In later years they increasingly based models on observations of real animals, either specimens collected during field trips or animals kept alive in aquaria in their house in Dresden. In 1879 Rudolf visited Northern Italy and the Adriatic coast to study marine biology and at about the same time an entire room in their house in Dresden was given over to aquaria, in which they kept specimens sent from various marine stations. They also visited several German Universities, and in particular they valued the assistance and friendship of Professor Ernst Haeckel of Jena. By 1880 Rudolf had become an active member of Isis, the Dresden Natural History Society, to whom he subsequently delivered two papers.

Comparison between early and later models made in the 1880s shows a distinct tendency towards increased scientific accuracy and away from a more showy early style. The emphasis had originally been on 'decoration for elegant rooms' and the models were described as such in the early catalogues. The Blaschkas were keen to accommodate customer demand and continued to increase their range accordingly. An early catalogue dating from 1871 listed nearly three hundred models. By 1888 the catalogue published by Henry Ward, their American agent, listed seven hundred!

The models varied greatly in complexity and in their method of construction. Component parts were formed from both clear and coloured glass, using a combination of glass blowing and lamp working techniques. The parts were then either directly fused together or assembled with adhesives, probably animal glues. Where necessary, other materials were used in the construction. Fine copper wires were often added to reinforce or attach delicate tentacles and gills and painted paper was cleverly incorporated to represent internal structures. They also made use of the actual shells of terrestrial, freshwater and

A source picture for the Paper Nautilus (*Argonata argo*) model

marine snails to which the modelled glass bodies of the animals were attached. These included a series of anatomical preparations that were almost certainly based on their own dissections of actual specimens.

Many of the Blaschkas' models came to be displayed at the Museum of Comparative Zoology at Harvard in the United States, where they were seen by Professor George Lincoln Goodale. He was planning new galleries in the adjacent Botanical Museum, and, in 1886, he visited the Blaschkas and persuaded them to make some sample flower models. He subsequently commissioned them to produce models of plants for his galleries, and in 1890 the Blaschkas were offered an exclusive ten-year contract with Harvard. Work on the animal models then ceased.

Leopold died in 1895, at the age of seventy-three, after which Rudolf continued working single-handedly until he retired in 1936. He died three years later at the age of eighty-two. By that time the collection consisted of 847 life-sized model plants and over 3,000 enlarged flowers and anatomical sections. Formally presented to the Botanical Museum of Harvard University in 1893, the entire collection had been privately financed as a memorial to the late Dr Charles Eliot Ware, a former Harvard graduate, by his widow and daughter. The plant models are displayed there to this day, attracting over 100,000 visitors annually.

Sadly, the same cannot be said of the collections of glass animals. Many have been lost over the years or, perhaps because of changing fashions, are no longer displayed.

Conserving the models

Our collection of Blaschka glass models has around 200 items. These represent a whole range of marine animals such as sea anemones, squid and jellyfish. The models have had a hard working life, and continue to be used in displays today. However, this has had an impact on the collection. Years of open display and poor storage conditions have caused damage to a large percentage of the collection. In addition, previous attempts to repair the specimens have caused further problems through the use of unsuitable repair materials

Conserving the Blaschka models is fraught with difficulties. Their age and complexity require an

A broken Paper Nautilus model

understanding of both how they were made and what they represent. Recent research work has looked closely at the Blaschkas' original notebooks and at the construction of the models themselves.
Past practice was to do as little as possible; however, with a renewed interest in the models emerging, the opportunity was taken to develop new displays demonstrating the fine workmanship of the Blaschkas. This in turn resulted in an active need to conserve parts of the collection.

The opportunity to conserve the models was both exciting and nerve-racking. These beautiful glass representations of marine animals were originally developed as educational models. Now they are increasingly considered to be works of art, with a value that makes them irreplaceable. The first important stage of any conservation project is to understand fully what the specimen or object represents, and then to understand the nature of the materials forming it. The Blaschka models are an intricate blend of glass, paint and textured coatings that have been put together to show the textures and colours of the animal in life. Amongst all this is the damage from past repairs and the accumulation of decades of dirt, which the conservator must rectify without damaging or altering the original model.

The conservation of the models involved a number of distinct processes. The first was to assess the most appropriate means of cleaning the models. Suitable methods then had to be developed for removing previous repairs. Finally, where required, the models needed to be repaired.

The models proved to be very difficult to clean. Surface finishes of paint and resin type materials had been applied to the outside of many of the specimens to add texture and colour. These had attracted surface dirt over the years, which was very

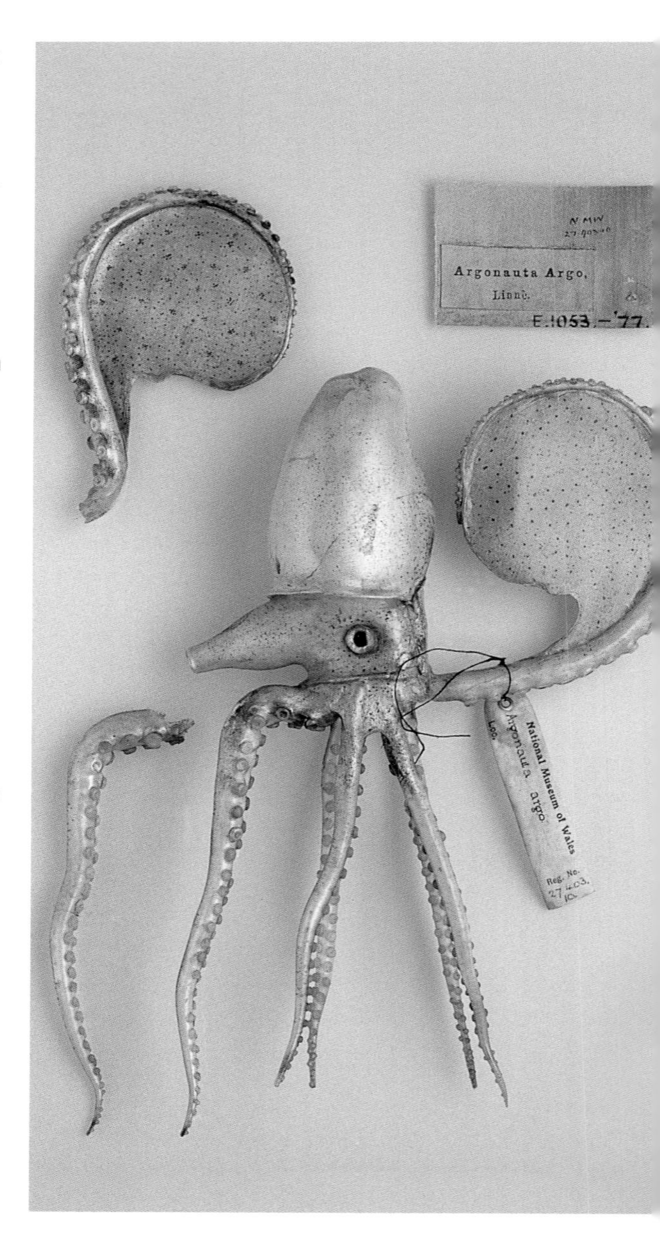

A detail of the damage to the Paper Nautilus model

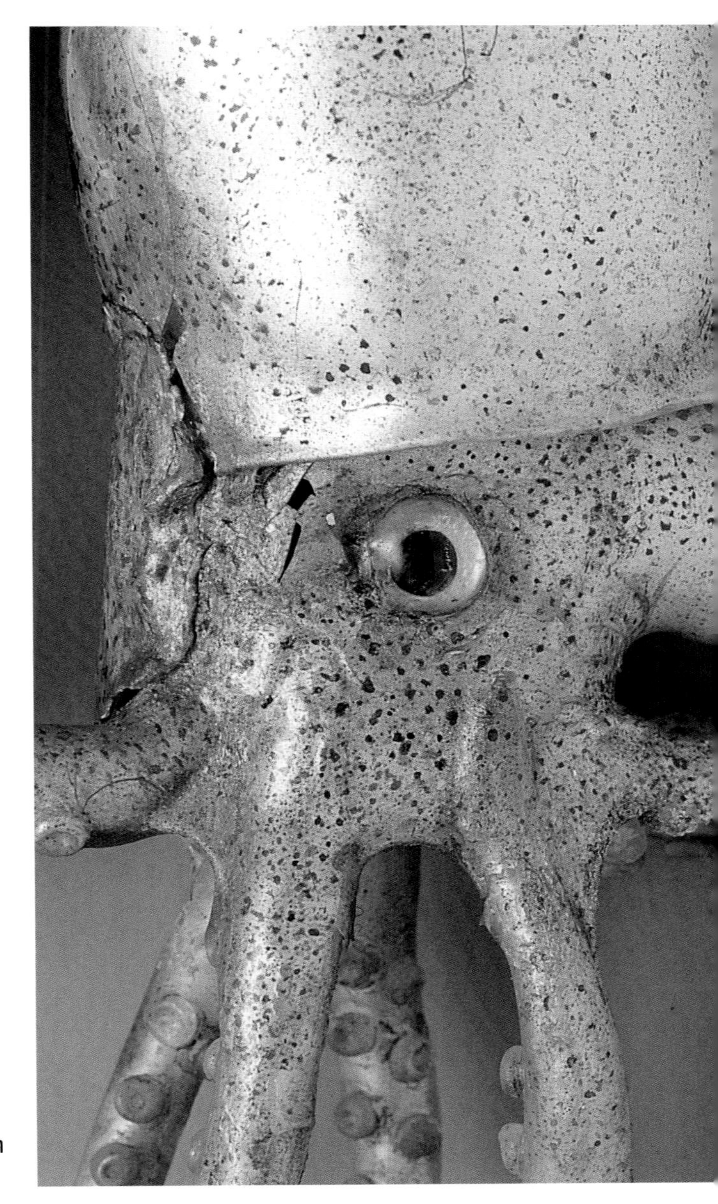

hard to remove. A range of solvents and cleaning solutions was carefully tested. The outcome was that whilst water (with a non-ionic detergent) proved effective for removing the dirt, the surface coatings were also soluble in this solution. Other solvents, such as acetone (propanone) were not effective. Only one of the solvents tested, white spirit, shifted any dirt without damaging the surface coatings. The cleaning that could be carried out was therefore very limited; only those specimens without a coloured or textured coating could be adequately cleaned.

Many of the specimens, especially the cephalopods, had become repeatedly broken and repaired over time. Many of these repairs were now discoloured or failing and some of them were also misplaced, for example tentacles had been re-attached in the wrong place. The older repairs tended to use animal glue that could easily be softened in water, but this required care where the surface coatings were present. The newer repairs appear to have used some general purpose adhesive which was found to be soluble in acetone. This adhesive was easy to soften and ultimately to remove. Once the old glues had been removed, consideration could then be given to reassembling the models.

The glass used to manufacture most of the models was found to be very thin and brittle. Some of the collection had been broken into numerous pieces, and, in the past, mistakes could have been made in the way the detached pieces were fitted together. Careful consideration had to be given to the adhesive to be used because the new repairs needed to be reversible. Epoxy resin based adhesives were quickly ruled out due to their strength of bond, lack of reversibility and long-term stability problems. The consolidant Paraloid B-72™ was chosen because it is a stable material that remains reversible and can

The reattached tentacle on the Paper Nautilus model

be removed if required. It is also forms a weak repair that will fail before the glass, reducing the chances of damaging the models further.

The refractive index of Paraloid B-72™ is not ideal for working with glass, but it does result in the repair remaining slightly visible, allowing future curators of the collection to identify previous conservation work. Paraloid B-72™ was used in two ways. The first method was as a contact adhesive: thin coatings were applied to the broken surfaces, which were joined when almost dry. The other method was as a film support. Films of Paraloid B-72™ were cast on acetate sheeting; these required several days' drying before they could be removed. The films remain reasonably flexible for a couple of weeks, and they were used to reinforce the edges of thin glass, or to form splints. The films were also used to fill gaps in some models where a section of tentacle or other process was missing.

The overall aim of this conservation project was to prepare the specimens for use in an exhibition on the Blaschka collection. The conservation work was

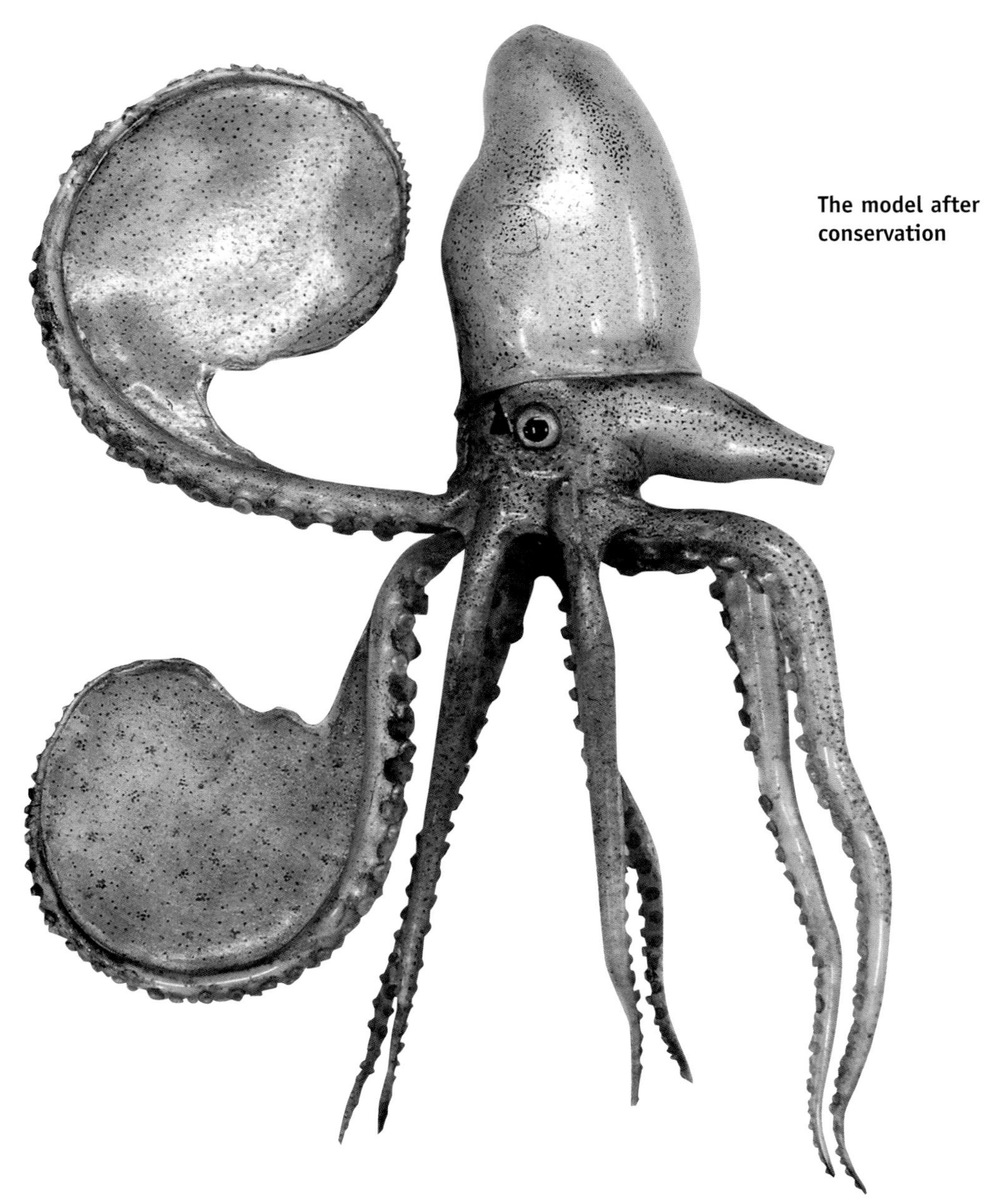

The model after conservation

developed to improve the visual appearance and integrity of the models, without further altering the original structure. Since completion of the work, many of the models have been part of a touring exhibition on the work of the Blaschkas, and have survived the experience very well!

The Blaschkas' glass models are an important collection, which is still used today. The recent work carried out on the collection will help ensure its continued survival for future generations to enjoy.

Chris Meechan and Julian Carter

Forging the firedog
Replicating an Iron Age masterpiece

A detail of the firedog's head

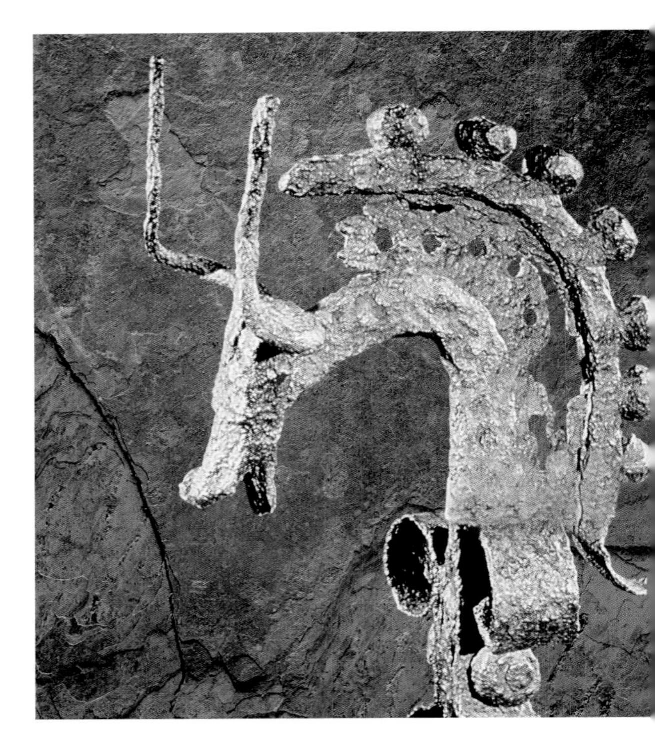

The Capel Garmon firedog is a masterpiece of Iron Age ironwork probably dating to the first century AD. The firedog was originally one of a pair of decorated stands used to roast meat over the open hearth at the centre of a round house. This exceptional piece was found by a man digging a ditch through a peat bog on the farm now known as Carreg Coedog, near Llanrwst, Gwynedd, in 1852. It was discovered lying on its side, with a large stone placed at each end. This careful positioning suggests that it was deliberately buried as an offering to the gods, and fits into a long-established prehistoric tradition of depositing metalwork in lakes, rivers and bogs.

In 1991, the firedog underwent a programme of X-radiography, which yielded new information about techniques used in its manufacture and the skills of the Iron Age blacksmith who made it. The condition of the iron used for the firedog was variable; some areas were visibly corroded and structurally weak, whereas in other areas the density and state of preservation of the iron, especially at the joints near the feet, left the images opaque to the highest kilovoltages available. Therefore clarification of the manufacturing techniques for certain areas was not fully possible, and the reconstruction was, to some extent, speculative.

David Petersen, the artist-blacksmith, was commissioned to make two replica Capel Garmon firedogs, one of which would form a conventional exhibit, while the second would demonstrate how it would have been used in an Iron Age round house (Petersen 1992). His discoveries while making the replicas complemented the X-radiographic work. The raw material available to the blacksmith was mild steel rather than the wrought iron of the original firedog, and therefore, of necessity, some of the techniques used were different from those of the original Iron Age blacksmith.

Iron was first used in Wales at around 750 BC, and from 300 BC onwards became increasingly employed for the production of weapons and tools. However, the Capel Garmon firedog stands apart from other artefacts of this period, not only because of its size, but also for the quality of the workmanship involved in its manufacture.

Although iron ores are relatively abundant compared to those of copper or tin, iron smelting was a difficult, time-consuming and very skilled operation. Iron was first produced in Europe many hundreds of years before temperatures that would melt this metal could be achieved, and so a

The complete firedog. Note the horns on the right-hand side are incorrectly mounted – they should stand vertical

succession of technological innovations were developed to allow early metallurgists to extract the iron from its ore. Britain is rich in iron ores, much of which could be gathered from opencast mines; the real feat was to separate the metal from the ore and for this it was necessary to introduce a powerful reducing agent plus an enormous amount of energy in the form of heat.

A clay or clay-lined airtight furnace was used, and charcoal was added into the furnace with the iron ore. These conditions result in the production of enough carbon monoxide at temperatures high enough to reduce iron ore to metallic iron. However, there were a number of other issues the limited technology of the period needed to overcome. Although small globules of metallic iron were formed, they were not molten, but remained solid and gradually coalesced, collecting in the form of a spongy mass of iron at the base of the furnace. Also, mixed in with the iron ore was a large amount of silica, alumina and lime (known as gangue), which also needed to be removed from the iron ore complex. These impurities combined in the furnace to form a slag, which is an artificial glass-like compound. Early slags consisted almost entirely of a mineral made up of iron and silicon oxides (fayalite, $2FeO.SiO_2$), which meant that much of the iron within the ore was used up and lost when the slag was formed. When a sizeable bloom of iron was built up that could be removed from the furnace, the smelt was complete.

There were so many potential problematic aspects to smelting – from collecting the right ores, to building a good furnace, to getting the charcoal and ore mix correct – that it is difficult to replicate such smelting successfully today, and it is very likely that there was magic and ritual meaning attached to a smelt, where stone could be seen transforming into metal, and important status conferred on those with the knowledge and powers to carry it out successfully (Herbert 1993).

The raw bloom produced at the end of a smelt was subjected to a series of alternate heating and hammering processes to expel the entrapped slag and consolidate the iron into a solid block of metal (Cleere 1976). It was at this point that the iron was fit for the blacksmith to work and shape at a forge. This was done by hammering and bending the iron when hot and manipulating it into the required forms.

Our wrought iron firedog consists of two vertical uprights each gracefully terminating in a curve shaped to resemble a horned ox-head with an elaborate mane or crest, and so contains aspects of both a bull and a horse. Savory (1976) refers to this as the 'extraordinary superimposition of what appears to be a classical helmet crest upon the oxen's necks'. Both uprights are supported and ornamented by two bands of looped iron ribbons riveted to the stems and feet. These loops would have held the roasting spit. The uprights are connected by a horizontal bar, attached at the base

An X-radiograph of the head, showing the mane crest, rivets and the curved top of the upright

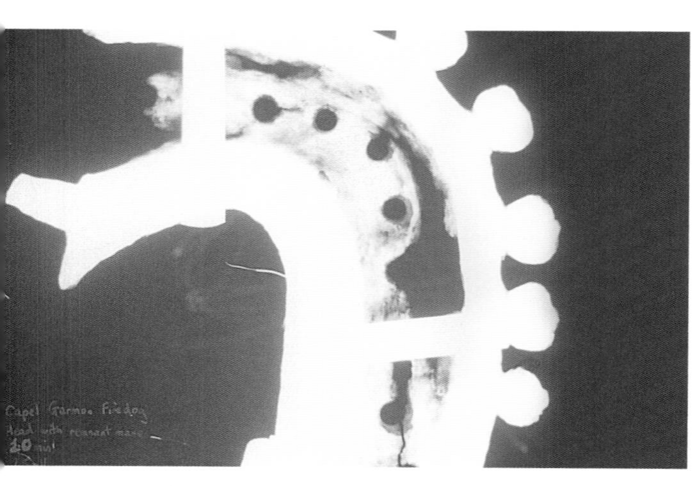

of each, and again supported by an ornamental band riveted between the stem and the horizontal bar. The feet are semi-circular bands, riveted both to the horizontal bar and to the bands supporting the vertical stems. The most recent description is in Piggott (Piggott 1971).

Previous treatments

At some stage after discovery the firedog was thickly coated with wax, a standard treatment until recently, used to preserve and consolidate ancient ironwork. Prior to the wax coating the firedog appears to have been either electrolytically or chemically stripped. Therefore little surface detail remains visible, and it is likely that any surface decoration has been lost. The firedog demonstrates such wonderful craftsmanship that it is not unlikely that some decorative surface ornamentation may originally have existed. The horns on the right hand side were also incorrectly mounted and should stand vertical.

Construction of the firedog

The complexity of the iron working can be illustrated with reference to the head and crest. The X-rays appear to show that each head consists of eighteen separate pieces of wrought iron (the vertical upright, the horned ox-head, a punched plate, a crest bar and seven rivets with seven separate applied heads). Each vertical upright has been bent at the top, widened towards the end, and terminates in a flange. The horned ox-head is a separate and distinct piece attached to the flange. The eyes, muzzle and nostrils have been modelled on each head. (The support straps between the mane crest and vertical upright are part of a modern reconstruction supporting the object and not an original feature.)

The mane or crest consists of a thin plate, punched with at least nine holes, and inserted between and into the bent part of the vertical upright and the topmost part of the crest. The X-rays showed clearly the upper part of each vertical upright had been split to take the mane plate, and each plate was bent into an approximate right angle for insertion into the bent vertical upright. The X-ray shows the plate is slightly broken at the most acute point of the curve.

The crest itself is a long bar of iron into which seven rivets, each with separately applied heads, have been inserted. It appears that the crest bar was originally twice its length and was bent back on itself and folded around the rivets and plate to hold them in place. A similar technique was used by David Petersen when making the replicas, and was confirmed by the X-ray. The X-ray clearly shows a line down the middle of the crest, indicating that the bar is in two pieces, welded on either side of each rivet, and finally welded together into a spiral coil at the lower end.

Components of the replicated firedog during manufacture (Image © David Petersen)

The X-ray shows that the bottom of each rivet stem has been hammered out onto the mane plate, possibly by splitting the rivet stem before inserting the plate into the split. This may also explain the thinness of the metal at the lower edge where it has been most worked. The crest bar was then welded around the mane plate, complete with the riveted stems, and finally the rivet heads individually applied to each rivet stem.

This incredible complexity and expertise of iron working was continued in manufacturing the stem, the foot and base assembly and the feet of the firedog.

Discounting the heads, it appears that twenty-six individual pieces of wrought iron comprise each upright and foot assembly. At present it is estimated that eighty-five separate pieces of wrought iron were used in the construction of the firedog. This includes thirty rivets with thirty-four separately applied heads.

Construction of the firedog is based heavily on riveting and the fact that worked iron contracts as it cools. Each riveted joint was hammered into position hot, in the knowledge that the rapid contraction of the joint on quenching would hold each piece firmly in place. The mane crest, however, was fire welded.

The weight of the finished firedog, deduced from an accurate replica made in 1968 by Alan Knight, would have been about 38kg. Peter Crew's work on the firedog, based on the known technology of later prehistoric iron-working in north-west Wales, enabled him to estimate that this amount of iron would have taken some three man-years' work to produce, requiring the smelting of some 800kg of ore and using about five tonnes of charcoal (Crew 1991). The final smithing and assembly of the firedog would have taken less than 5 per cent of this time. In constructing the replica firedogs for the exhibition *Celts in Wales*, David Petersen, with an assistant smith and two apprentices, took six weeks to make two firedogs, starting with stock mild steel. This compares favourably with the 300 hours of workshop time taken by Alan Knight in 1968, using good quality wrought iron.

The Capel Garmon firedog demonstrates an impressive mastery of iron-working technology, and it implies that the work is the culmination of years of work and experience. Before starting, the blacksmith must have worked out the order in which he intended to put the firedog together,

David Petersen at work in his forge (Image © David Petersen)

and he would have employed a number of skilled assistants to help. X-radiography has given further insights into the enormous skill and craftsmanship involved – and inspires huge admiration for the blacksmith who masterminded the work.

The tenth-century Welsh laws attributed to Hywel Dda (Jenkins 1990) specify levels of compensation to be paid for the death of individuals of different skills, reflecting, in effect, their value to their society. For instance, a blacksmith's value is three times that of a warrior. Examination of the Capel Garmon firedog indicates clearly why this was so. Despite all the discoveries that have been made in the past 150 years, it remains one of the most important pieces of early decorative ironwork to have been found in Britain.

Kate Hunter and David Petersen.

The completed replica

CLEERE, H. 1976. Ironmaking, 127-141. In STRONG, D. & BROWN, D. (eds). *Roman Crafts*. Duckworth, London.

CREW, P. 1991. The experimental production of prehistoric bar-iron. *Historical Metallurgy*, 25, 21-36.

HERBERT, E. W. 1993. *Iron, gender and power: rituals of transformation in African societies*. Indiana University Press, Bloomington, USA.

JENKINS, D. 2000. *Hywel Dda, The Law*. The Welsh Classics v. 2, Gomer Press, Llandysul, Dyfed (first published in 1986).

PETERSEN, D. 1992. Capel Garmon Firedogs. *British Blacksmith*, 63, 10-11.

PIGGOTT, S. 1971. Firedogs in Iron Age Britain and beyond, 251-252. In BOARDMAN, J., BROWN, M. A. & POWELL, T. G. E. (eds). *The European Community in Later Prehistory: studies in honour of F.C. Hawkes*. Routledge & Kegan Paul, London.

SAVORY, H. N. 1976. *Guide Catalogue of the Early Iron Age Collections*. National Museum of Wales, Cardiff.

Construction of the firedog

The stem

The bottom of the uprights terminates in the horizontal bar and then the feet. These areas were too dense to get clear X-rays, but those that were obtained appear to show that the two shorter decorative support bands, between stem and horizontal bar, are attached by rivets. Rivets are inserted into the upright but not as extensively hammered in as those observed on the mane crest. Subsequently, the ornamental bands were coiled over at the top, probably as much for support as ornamentation. The same coiled technique can be seen at the other end of each band where they are riveted to the horizontal bar, and again where the two longer bands are attached to the two vertical uprights.

Each upright is supported by two decorative, but functional, bands of iron, attached via three rivets to the upright and a fourth rivet to the semi-circular bar making up each foot. There is some surface evidence that the coils may originally have been decorated with a design of three parallel lines.

The foot and base assembly

The method of attachment between the upright, the horizontal bar and the foot is unclear. However, the method adopted by David Petersen corresponds with the available

An exploded diagram of the firedog (Image by Tony Daly, after David Petersen)

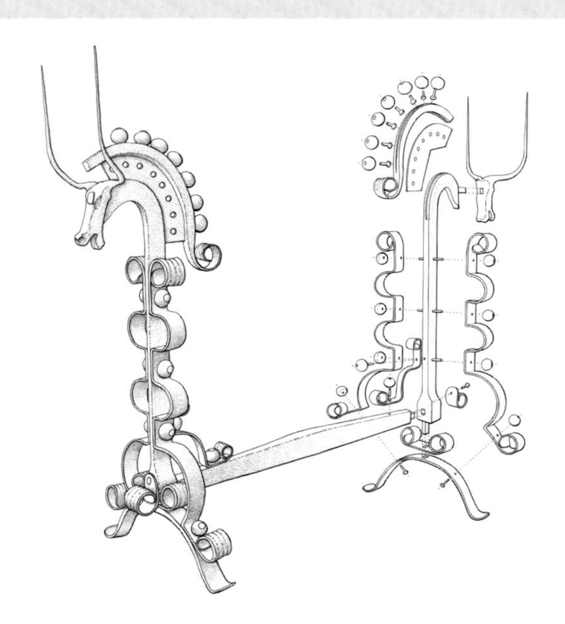

evidence. The base of each vertical upright is an upset shape terminating in a flange. A squared hole has been punched through the upset. Each end of the horizontal bar terminates in a flange, which fits into the upset to make a squared tenon joint. Finally a plate attached via a blind rivet has been set into the upset, possibly to hide the join.

The feet

Each foot assembly comprises the flanged vertical upright, riveted through a decorative band to the semi-circular bar, which is the foot. The flange was attached under the bar by hammering. The strength of the joint relies upon contraction of the iron when cooling. A coiled iron bar was riveted between each foot and the horizontal bar. The coils are tightly curved into the upset stem, possibly to give added stability. The whole firedog is extremely heavy, and therefore the means of attachment between firedog and feet was important for stability.

X-radiography

X-radiography is used in hospitals to reveal internal details of the human body; the same technique can also be used by conservators and museum curators to discern what is underneath the corroded and encrusted surface of an object, or behind the upper paint layers on a painting.

X-radiography works by exposing the object to high-energy electromagnetic waves or X-rays. The results have traditionally been recorded on photographic film, though increasingly X-rays are being viewed digitally, and on real time machines via fluorescent screens that allow an object to be rotated as it is viewed.

In museums X-rays are used for examining a huge variety of material, from watermarks on paintings to the innards of industrial appliances. When X-rays are directed at the object, some radiation will pass through it onto the film, whereas some is absorbed by the object. The amount absorbed depends on several factors, including the energy (kV) of the radiation, the thickness of the material and its elemental composition. Heavier, denser materials appear lighter on X-radiographs, as fewer X-rays have penetrated.

In order to achieve the optimum image for the material being examined, the type of machine and the operating conditions need to be carefully selected.

There are three main ways of controlling the X-rays from standard machines:

- The current (in milliamps; mA) controls the intensity of the radiation, more electrons are produced and therefore more X-rays, and this in effect reduces the amount of time required for each exposure.
- The energy (in kilovolts; kV) will alter the penetrative qualities of the X-rays; higher kVs are used to penetrate metals.
- Where the mA cannot be altered on some machines, the exposure time can be varied to achieve similar results.

LANG, J. & MIDDLETON, A. 1997. *Radiography of Cultural Material*. Butterworth Heinemann, Oxford.

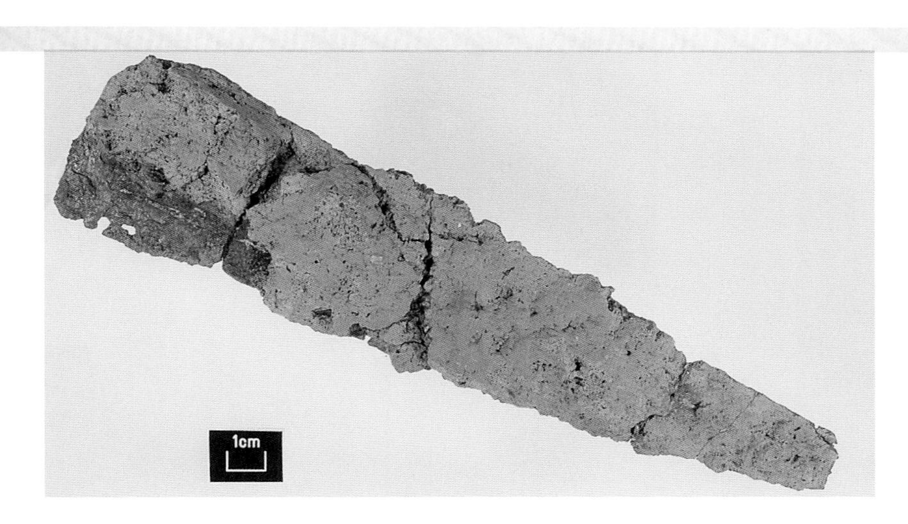

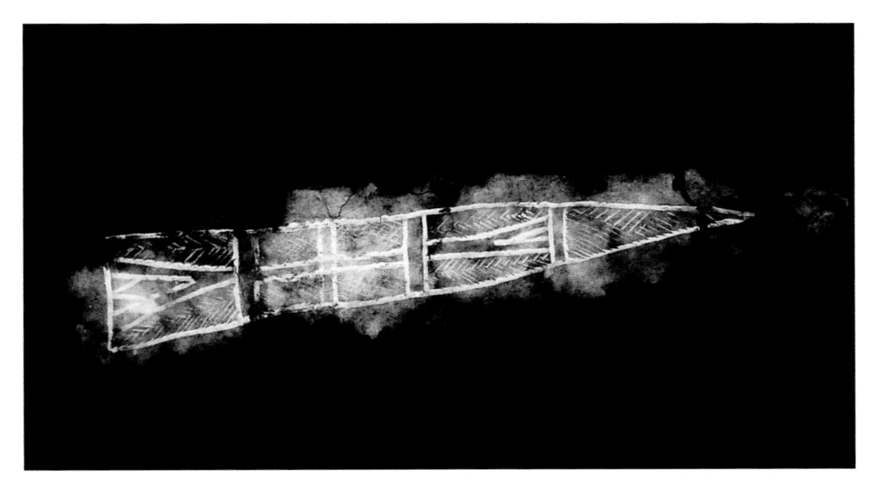

The Loughor scabbard plate. Archaeological iron objects are usually X-rayed. Voluminous and distorting corrosion products often means their original form is hidden. X-rays offer a quick and cost-effective method of assessing objects. The images produced provide a permanent record of actual size and condition and often reveal detail that might not be seen any other way

Tracking dinosaurs
Footprints on a Welsh shore

Casts of original specimens fulfil many roles in the conservation of palaeontological material. Certain specimens are highly unstable, for example those that are prone to pyrite decay. A cast can be made so that if decay occurs and the fossil deteriorates a permanent record remains. This is especially important if they are 'type material', that is, individual specimens from which a new species has been described. Casts can be used for many educational purposes, for example for handling collections, so that original fragile and delicate specimens need not be used. They can provide wider access for both specialists and the public to rare and unique fossils that would otherwise be unavailable. Moulds can also be taken in the field when it is undesirable or impossible to remove a specimen.

Dinosaur bones are a relatively rare occurrence in the fossil record, whereas the fossilised remains of their tracks and trails are more common. Some sites in North America contain many millions of individual tracks covering hundreds of square kilometres. These tracks record the actions of a single moment and can provide palaeontologists with a range of information about how dinosaurs moved and how they reacted to their environment. Due to the scale of these fossils, casting is often the only method of preserving the

A reconstruction of a Triassic floodplain in south Wales (© John Sibbick)

record if the trackway is under threat, for example from erosion.

One of the most prolific and important dinosaur sites in Britain is found on the coast in south Wales. In 1996 a unique trackway was discovered and a cast was made of the surface. The task was complicated, as the location of the track was below the high water mark.

Geological background

In south Wales, rocks of Upper Triassic and Lower Jurassic age (about 220-195 million years old) form quite extensive outcrops along the Vale of Glamorgan coast. These rocks show that, during the Upper Triassic, this part of south Wales was a low-lying, hot desert abutting a large lagoon-like lake, which by the early Jurassic had been inundated by a warm, shallow sea. Although a desert climate prevailed, periods of heavy rain did occur from time to time, which led to extensive flash flooding of the desert floor.

On the coast between Sully and Barry, the Upper Triassic rocks are continuously exposed in a series of extensive rocky shore platforms and low cliffs. The rocks themselves consist of a series of fine-grained red siltstones, yellow/grey sandstones and

Applying the silicon rubber

some very coarse pebble-beds (conglomerates). All of these lie almost horizontally on top of much older, highly folded beds of Carboniferous Limestone (approximately 330 million years old). The Triassic conglomerates contain well-rounded pebbles of predominantly Carboniferous Limestone and have been interpreted as sediments that were deposited during periods of heavy rain in the beds of ephemeral rivers (wadis) that drained southwards across the desert floor. The finer grained sandstones represent sheets of sand that spilled out across the desert floor when the rivers burst their banks while the fine, red silty deposits were laid down on the desert floor itself. Within the siltstone succession are a number of horizons where fossil ripples and mudcracks are preserved. These show that short-lived lakes were formed, which then rapidly dried out. It is within the siltstone succession that dinosaur footprints and trackways occur at a number of different horizons.

Before 1974 the only dinosaur footprints known from south Wales were those found in rocks of Upper Triassic age at Newton Nottage, near Porthcawl, in 1878 and at nearby Nottage Court sometime before 1927 (Lockley et al. 1996). However, in 1974 over 450 mainly small (5-6 cms long), three-toed dinosaur footprints that covered an area of approximately

Removing the mould from the trackway

25 m^2 were found at the Bendricks, near Barry (Tucker & Burchette 1977). Subsequent further examination of the succession in the Bendricks area located many more footprints and some well-preserved trackways. By 1996, tracks representing at least four different types of animal (mainly dinosaurs) had been found from ten different levels within the succession making this the most extensive area of Upper Triassic dinosaur footprint tracks in Britain and possibly Europe (Benton & Spencer 1995). Its importance led to the area being declared a Site of Special Scientific Interest (SSSI) in 1996.

Due to damage by ill-informed fossil collectors, the surface discovered in 1974 was lifted in 1977 and removed to the Museum where, after cleaning and conservation, nearly 90 per cent of the original surface was eventually re-laid within the Evolution of Wales gallery in the National Museum Cardiff. Two well-preserved parallel trackways, discovered on a surface below high water mark at the western end of the section in 1990, were also removed as they would ultimately have been degraded and destroyed by marine erosion. Part of these can also be viewed in the same exhibition.

New quadrupedal trackway

Before 1996 all of the trackways found at the Bendricks were of animals walking on two legs. However, in autumn 1996, a single trackway of an animal walking on all fours was found on a large fallen block of red siltstone at the bottom of the cliff on the east side of the Bendricks. On falling away from the cliff the block had split in two horizontally, to expose a finely mudcracked surface on the top of the lower piece. On this surface was imprinted a trackway 174 cm long, comprising six four-toed tracks of an animal walking on all fours. The gait of the animal was such that the tracks from the smaller front feet were very close to, and sometimes cut by, the imprint of the rear foot. The tracks are thought to have been made by a relatively small prosauropod dinosaur similar to *Plateosaurus* or *Thecodontosaurus*. Because the block lay on an exposed part of the foreshore, well below high tide level, it was subject to heavy marine erosion and the footprint surface would rapidly have been destroyed. The thickness of the bed in which the trackway was preserved, and the problems that cutting and storing large slabs of footprints pose, led to the decision to take a mould from the trackway in situ in order to produce a permanent cast.

Moulding the trackway

Moulding the trackway posed two major problems: first, because the block was located below high tide level, the moulding had to be completed between tides; second, the weather could affect this process. The position of the block on the middle foreshore meant that the tidal window was about six hours. Moulding was to be undertaken in April, and the only time when a low tide occurred in the middle of the day was during a period of high spring tides.

A moulding medium was required that would provide a good definition of the footprints, while curing quickly despite the cool spring weather. It was decided that a silicone rubber would provide the best definition of the footprints, with a fast-acting catalyst added to reduce the curing time.

Moulding started just as the tide was receding from the block. Before this could begin, the surface of the slab had to dry, which, due to the cool weather, took longer than had been calculated. The area was cleared of loose material, such as sand, as the trackway dried, and then the area to be moulded was bounded by a plasticene wall 4 cm high to contain the silicone rubber. Once the slab was dry, the silicone rubber and the catalyst were mixed in 500g lots and applied. The slab was at an angle, so the silicon rubber was poured on at the highest point, and allowed to flow downwards until a thin skim covered the whole trackway. Once the area was covered the silicone rubber took just over one hour to cure.

Time constraints meant that it was not possible to apply many thin layers to the area. Instead, a thickening agent was added to the mix. This resulted in a mixture with the texture of butter-cream icing, which could be spread thickly on top of the thin skim. (If this had been used from the outset, without the underlying thin area, definition would have been lost.) Once the thickened silicon rubber was applied, gauze bandages were gently pressed into the top surface of the rubber to protect the mould from tearing. This top layer took approximately one hour to cure, after which the mould was removed gradually from the block and rolled ready for transport back to the Museum, where it was then laid flat. Only a few small pieces of sediment adhered to the mould, and other than that no apparent damage was done to the block or trackway.

The only major problems encountered during the moulding of the trackway were two heavy showers of rain. However, the rock surface was not exposed during either of these showers, because the first occurred just after the thin layer of silicone rubber had been applied and the second during the application of the thick upper layer. Throughout the duration of the showers, a plastic sheet was held over the area. Water did pond slightly at the bottom of the specimen but this was easily mopped up and did not damage the mould in any way.

Casting

Two casts were required from the mould, one for the Museum and the other for an expert on dinosaur trackways in the USA. The mould was cleaned with water and a non-ionic detergent. Casts were made from polyester resin, with opaque colourants added. The surface of the cast was painted with acrylic paints to simulate the natural colour of the original rock as far as possible. The back of the cast was strengthened with fibreglass, and Correx™ (fluted plastic sheeting) was used to give it rigidity.

Postscript

The original trackway has continued to erode and a large section of it has now broken away: the mould and casts will soon be the only record of this unique specimen.

Caroline Buttler and Stephen Howe

BENTON, M. J. & SPENCER, P. S. 1995. *Fossil reptiles of Britain*. Geological Conservation Review Series, Joint Nature & Conservation Committee.

LOCKLEY, M. G., KING, M., HOWE, S. & SHARPE, T. 1996. Dinosaur tracks and other archosaur footprints from the Triassic of South Wales. *Ichnos*, 5, 23-41.

TUCKER, M. E. & BURCHETTE, T. P. 1977. Triassic dinosaur footprints from South Wales: their context and preservation. *Palaeogeography, Palaeoclimatology, Palaeoecology,* 22, 195-208.

Forever green
Botanical wax models

The botanical collections at the National Museum of Wales house over 250,000 dried herbarium specimens. This is a very valuable scientific resource, but dried botanical specimens can lose colour, shape and texture and are therefore of limited use for display or educational purposes. However, we also have a collection of approximately 1,500 botanical wax models. Wax is a good medium to use for botanical models as it depicts the life-like qualities of the plants and enables the accurate representation of rare or even extinct plant material in all seasons, which is both highly desirable and beneficial in a museum context.

The collection includes portrayals of Welsh flora as well as specimens from other parts of Britain and Europe. It dates back to the 1900s, and is still developing and growing today. Some of the models were acquired from other institutions, such as the Science Museum, while others were made by botanical artists working at the Museum. Eveline Jenkins was the first such artist, working from the 1930s; over a twenty-year period, she created many excellently crafted models of fungi. Roy Herbert replaced her in the 1960s and made many of the finer vascular models held in the collection; he retired in the 1980s.

The collections were well looked after when the artists were in employment. However, once they left, the models became neglected due to a lack of the knowledge and skill required for repairing and maintaining wax models. In the early 1990s it was realised that there was a serious long-term threat to the collection, and a conservation project was initiated to examine their storage conditions and investigate the composition of the models in relation to their condition.

Part of the wax model collection is on display in

Damaged wax models

the natural history galleries at the National Museum Cardiff, but the majority is in storage. The collections were stored in two different locations, and one concern was that the environmental conditions in these stores might have been having a deleterious effect on the wax. The models had also been subjected to poor handling procedures; the accession numbers and plant names were frequently missing, so the models were not stored in any particular order.

The project began with a survey to determine the condition, the exact location of all the models, and the effect of the surrounding environment on them.

The main factors that contribute to wax degradation are extremes or fluctuations in temperature and relative humidity, and contact with certain metal ions (especially copper and iron). Excessive exposure to visible and ultraviolet light can also cause wax to deteriorate. Ideally, wax should be stored at stable environments between 13°-20°C and with a relative humidity of 50-60 per cent. The two locations used for storage were a general large botany store and a small room that also contained three freezers used for pest control.

The environment in both locations was monitored for the duration of the project. Conditions in the small room were warm and dry (25°C and 30 per cent relative humidity), whereas the main store was air-conditioned with an apparently suitable and stable relative humidity and temperature (20°C and 50 per cent relative humidity) for the storage of wax models. Unexpectedly, however, the survey revealed that the models housed within the small room were in better condition. It was also apparent that degradation was occurring in the same places on all of the models, irrespective of mechanical damage from handling and storage. Not surprisingly, deterioration was occurring at joins or where excess stress had been incurred, but it was also taking place where large amounts of wax had been employed on some areas of the models; fine detailed areas such as flowers or petals were in a better condition. In some areas, the structural wires used to strengthen and form the stems of the plants had become exposed, and when no longer protected by wax layers these had begun to corrode.

It was thought that the age and composition of the wax must have been the determining factor for deterioration and not environment. As various materials had been incorporated into the models and rarely documented by the artists, their composition had to be analysed. This was carried out before any conservation work could commence.

Gas chromatography identified the larger areas of wax as mixtures of beeswax and paraffin wax, and in some cases Canada balsam or ceresin. The finer areas such as the flowers were purely beeswax, which is very stable. Paraffin wax is less stable and with time it releases solvents that cause the already hard wax to become more brittle. However it also increases the working time for the modeller, and in practical terms a mixture of both waxes is often necessary for working larger areas of a model. Fluctuations in environmental conditions or mechanical damage would increase the instability already present in these areas and cause further cracking. The warmer environment of the small store, containing the freezers, was possibly helping the wax to remain a little more malleable, so that less stress was induced when the objects were handled.

Although the models made from pure beeswax were generally in a better condition, there were some discrepancies between a few models of similar periods. On the models where the wax was coloured it appeared to be de-laminating and cracking and was covered in a white bloom. It is thought that unfavourable conditions can produce this bloom as a result of the movement of fatty acids from within the wax structure to the surface. Also, at the time of modelling, the speed with which the wax cools can affect the size of its crystals. Slower cooling is thought to produce smaller, more stable polymorphic

Wax models, after conservation

Bloom on the leaf of a wax model

A Carboniferous fossil cone

forms. Rapid cooling, however, produces larger, less stable crystals, and fatty acids would therefore have more room to move around and migrate to the surface of the wax forming the characteristic bloom (Pearlstein 1986). Fatty acids act as plasticisers, and so if they are lost through migration the model will become more brittle and will crack (Warth 1956). However, the uncoloured models within the collection showed little deterioration and no surface bloom.

To investigate this problem experiments were set up involving the systematic application of pigments to beeswax, paraffin wax and wax mixtures when molten, and the external application of various solvents. The speed of cooling the wax samples was standard throughout. The results showed that on the waxes mixed with pigments, the surface bloomed after just two weeks, and the intensity of this bloom varied with different colours. When studied under a microscope, the surface of the coloured wax was covered in a thick layer of fine crystals. The application of solvents to the wax surface also altered the bloom. No bloom was visible on the uncoloured waxes.

Once the analysis and experiments were completed remedial work was carried out on the models requiring attention. Beeswax alone was recommended for the repair work, as it is stable and softer than the paraffin and beeswax mix. To prevent the bloom occurring on the repairs, pigments were not incorporated into the melted wax; instead the repairs were painted afterwards with oil paint, which also provided a protective surface coating.
Some models were dusted with a soft dry brush and cleaned with distilled water and cotton buds – but only when really necessary. Once repaired, the models were mounted onto Perspex™ and secured in position with moulded polycarbonate rod.
This method of mounting offers non-abrasive support to the delicate models, preventing movement and protecting them when handled. All of the models were rehoused in custom-made Correx™ boxes or ready-made acid free boxes, and lined with Plastazote™ to reduce movement. The models were all identified, verified against the original registers and labelled with the correct updated botanical

A wax model of a cone

names. The collection was then all placed in the cooler, larger store on static shelving, and arranged in alphabetical order by Latin name. This meant that the collection was fully accessible to staff and visitors for the first time in its existence. The models have also been entered onto the collection management database, which will eventually allow even greater access when the collection becomes available as a catalogue.

The repair work ensured that the models were more stable and should therefore help prevent future damage and reduce the corrosion of exposed wire supports. The repair of the wax models brought some ethical considerations to the fore. Standard conservation ethics often follow guidelines that do not always take account of the variety of roles of accessioned items. The function of these models in a museum context is subtly different from the objects they represent, and from many other areas of the collection. They have been made as museum pieces, and have since acquired an historical value in their own right. Unlike some other methods of model making and replication, these have not been superseded by other methods of display but are still used to produce important functioning items within the exhibitions. To repair with wax is bonding like with like, therefore the repair can never be removed again without taking some of the original wax with it. The wax also has to be heated to form a very strong and flexible bond to support the extremely delicate model. Although traditionally it is important from a conservation point of view that repairs are detectable and reversible, it is not always possible to apply this to natural history collections. The wax models are accurate representations of real botanical specimens, and if the repair is too obvious it could be construed as an identifying characteristic of a species.

Paleobotanical wax model making

The tradition of botanical wax model-making continues today at the Museum but it is not confined to recreating modern-day plants. Fossil plants are now also being recreated in a three-dimensional form.

Our Palaeobotanists researching the Late

Carboniferous coal measure forests can theoretically reconstruct the plants from this extinct vegetation by piecing together fossil remains, but these concepts are very difficult to illustrate.

One solution is to produce illustrative drawings and paintings of what the plants might have looked like, which are very useful in books but less effective for displays. Therefore, in the context of the collection of wax models, it seemed a natural development to start modelling these fossil plants in the same way. Wax appeared to be the perfect medium, as it can be sculpted and easily altered once set. This proved to be an important factor when modelling these extinct plants. A great deal of consultation and reinterpretation was necessary during the process, as so much of the detail is unknown or has been distorted by fossilisation.

Before the project began, information on the modelling of living plants was gathered, and models from the existing collection were examined to gain a further understanding of the methods used in their construction. Recognition of unsuitable materials and weakness in the structure of the older models enabled the new ones to be constructed in a way that, it was hoped, would avoid repeating past problems and make the models easier to look after in the future.

Several experiments were undertaken before the best methods and materials were established. These were sometimes in conflict with the experiments carried out on the stability of the waxes, and compromises had to be found to enable realistic models to be manufactured. Generally, a mixture of beeswax and paraffin wax was used, the proportions of the two depending on the complexity of the area being modelled. Although it had been proven that beeswax was most stable when used alone, it has a very fast setting time and can only be successfully used in smaller detailed areas. Adding paraffin wax increases the working time. Beeswax is also very expensive, and this, in conjunction with its working properties, did not recommend its use for large areas of the models. Although the addition of colourants had contributed to the deterioration of the wax on the historical models, true realistic representations could not be achieved without incorporating colours into the wax to form a base colour. Experiments with a range of colourants showed that oil paints and refined dry ground artist's pigments caused least problems with blooming. Oil paints were chosen for these models as they blended well with the wax and gave a more workable consistency to the medium. The waxes were melted together in metal baking trays over a hot plate, and oil paints were mixed directly into the molten wax to achieve the desired colours.

The models were constructed in sections. The main internal structure of large sections was formed from materials that would remain inert whilst in contact with the surrounding wax coating. Paper, cardboard, glass, tissue, Perspex and natural fabrics such as silk could all be coated with molten wax using a paintbrush.

Leaf shapes and other plant organs were made from sheets of tissue paper or silk; these materials absorbed the wax much better than synthetic fibres, and were especially useful for making delicate areas. Structures could be dipped into the molten wax then slowly withdrawn, allowing the surplus wax to drain off. Patterns could then be cut from the sheets with scissors or surgical scalpels. Fine details such as plant hairs were achieved by dipping thin nylon or cotton threads into the wax and applying the individual fibres to the models. Metal was generally avoided, but tinned copper wire proved useful for plant stems and leaves. The various parts were then fused together using metal dental tools heated to the correct temperature over a Bunsen flame. A hot air torch was used to fuse sections of the wax together without having to handle the surface

The models were then painted with oil paint, which has a good even coverage and is easy to blend and remove. Good colours are crucial for the plants to be convincing, but are also the least certain factor when reconstructing extinct species. An attempt was made to relate colours to the living plant families, but guesswork was sometimes inevitable. To make the plant look more realistic, different finishes were created by thinning the paints and using acrylic varnishes. The results ranged from a matt effect to a glossy sheen. As well as adding colour and texture, these final external coats help protect the wax from blooming.

When a model was finished, all relevant details were noted in the conservation records. These included diagrams showing exactly what combinations of materials were used in different parts of the model and the date the model was made. Any surplus wax and spare parts were attached to the records, and can be used in the future as replacements if the model is ever damaged.

One of the most important functions of museums is to communicate to their visitors the knowledge, research and understanding that lies behind the specimens in their care. In the case of the plant fossils, these models are a powerful display technique using realistic three-dimensional images to recreate what the living plants would have looked like. These models have made a considerable impact in exhibitions and lectures, and enabled concepts such as fossilisation and the relationship between these extinct plants and their modern counterparts to be explained much more clearly.

A reconstruction of a Carboniferous landscape (by Annette Townsend)

Victoria Purewal and Annette Townsend

Code of Ethics and Rules of Practice of the United Kingdom Institute of Conservation

HARLEY, C. 1993. A Note on the Crystal Growth on the Surface of a Wax Artifact. *Studies in Conservation*, 38, 63-66.

PEARLSTEIN, E. 1986. Fatty bloom on wood sculpture from Mali. *Studies in Conservation*, 31, 83-91.

WARTH, A. H. 1956. *The Chemistry and Technology of Wax*. Reinhold Publishing Co., New York.

Glossary

Alkyl ketene dimer (AKD): A synthetic sizing agent used in paper in the form of an emulsion.

Annealing: The process whereby work hardened (brittle) metal is heated to reform the microscopic grain structure of the solid metal, making it malleable once more, so shaping can continue.

Anoxic: Without oxygen.

Anoxic storage: see page 32.

Antioxidant: A substance that inhibits oxidation.

Autolytic decay: The destruction of tissues or cells of an organism by the action of substances that are produced within the organism itself.

Base pairs: In double-stranded nucleic acids, a 'base pair' is the structure formed between two complementary nucleotides by hydrogen bonding. In DNA, adenine (A) pairs with thymine (T) and cytosine (C) pairs with guanine (G). The number of base pairs in a piece of DNA is a means of estimating the size of the molecule.

Biodiversity: The variety of life in all its forms, levels and combinations. Includes ecosystem diversity, species diversity and genetic diversity.

Buffering of paper: The addition of an alkaline reserve within the paper to combat acidity longterm.

Cadw: The Welsh Historic Monuments Executive Agency, which is part of Welsh Assembly Government. It is responsible for the conservation, presentation and promotion of the built heritage of Wales. Cadw is a Welsh word which means 'to keep'.

Carboniferous: The geological period that extends from about 360 to 300 million years ago.

Cephalopod: A marine mollusc characterized by well-developed head and eyes and sucker-bearing tentacles.

Ceresin: A white wax extracted from ozocerite, a paraffin wax.

Cinquefoil: An ornamental carving consisting of five arcs arranged in a circle.

Cist: A stone-lined burial chamber.

Correx™: An extruded cellular polypropylene sheet, rather like a plastic version of corrugated card.

Critical point drying: A specialist method for drying specimens that avoids the problems of shrinkage caused by normal drying procedures. Water in the specimen is replaced by a fluid such as liquid CO_2, avoiding setting up a liquid/gas interface, and then the fluid is allowed to vaporise by raising the temperature above the critical point, the temperature at which the liquid state no longer occurs.

Deliquescence: The process by which a soluble salt absorbs water from the air to form a solution.

Dendritic structure: A three-dimensional scatter of fern-like branches formed when a metal alloy is cast and slowly cooled. The rate of cooling influences the size of dendrites: the faster they cool, the smaller the grain size.

Dendrochronology: Archaeological dating technique that uses the growth rings of long-lived trees as a calendar.

DNA cloning: The production of multiple, exact replicas of a single gene or other segment of DNA.

Endpapers: The extra, protective and decorative leaves at the front and back of a book; the 'flyleaf' is the loose page separating the text from the boards, while the 'pastedown' lines the cover.

Esparto: Species of grass native to Spain, Portugal and North Africa, producing greyish-green leaves which are used in the manufacture of paper, cordage, ropes, baskets, mats, and cloth, etc.

Ethyl alcohol: C_2H_5OH: A flammable organic compound formed during sugar fermentation. It is also called ethanol, grain alcohol or simply alcohol.

Equation of time: see page 129.

Fatty acids: A long-chained organic acid (or carboxylic acid), found in fats.

Formaldehyde: CH_2O (methanal). Primary aldehyde that is very soluble in water. Used as a protein fixative to preserve biological tissues.

FTIR: see page 144.

Freeze drying: see page 48.

Gas chromatography: A technique for separating chemical substances by taking advantage of differences in the rates at which they are adsorbed from a moving stream of gas by a stationary material. It is widely used for the separation and identification of chemical compounds of organic origin.

Genetics: The study of heredity and variation in organisms. It can also refer to the genetic features of an organism.

Genome: The complete DNA sequence, containing all genetic information and supporting proteins, in the chromosomes of an individual or species.

Genomic DNA: The complete DNA molecule, containing all genetic information.

Histopathology: Pathology concerned with the tissue changes characteristic of disease.

Hydrolysis: A chemical reaction in which a compound reacts with water, resulting in its decomposition or alteration.

Impasto: Thickly applied, raised, textured areas of paint made by the artist's brushwork.

Industrial methylated spirits (IMS): Ethanol with small quantities of methanol and sometimes pyridine and dye to render it unfit for consumption.

Infra-red reflectography: Method of examination with infra-red light, commonly used to show dark underdrawing on top of a light coloured ground layer.

Kevlar™: The commercial name for poly(p-phenylene terephtalamide). It is a light but strong material used in applications such as bullet proof vests, brake pads and aircraft tyres.

Klucel G™: (Hydroxypropylcellulose) a non-ionic cellulose ether with a combination of properties often used in paper and book conservation. Soluble in many polar organic solvents and extremely flexible without plasticisers in films and coatings.

Layer structure: Layers of paint found in a work, usually ground/priming, underpainting and then one or more layers of paint.

Lignin: A component of the cell walls of plants which contributes to their strength and rigidity.

Lithology: The description of rocks based on characteristics such as colour, mineralogical composition and grain size.

Lost wax casting: A process of casting in which an object is modelled in wax and covered in a clay mould. The wax is melted and poured out, and the space is filled with molten metal to form the shape of the original wax model.

Lyme's disease: Lyme's disease is caused by the bacterium *Burrelia burgdorferi* that is carried by infected ticks. It is found on many animals including deer and squirrels.

MDA: Museum Documentation Association.

Morphology: The study of form and structure of animals and plants and their fossil remains.

Nucleotide: Building blocks of DNA and RNA. Nucleotides consist of phosphate, sugar and one of four bases, adenine, guanine, cytosine and uracil (RNA) or thymine (DNA). Thousands of nucleotides are linked to form a DNA or RNA molecule.

Nanometre: (nm) one billionth of a meter, 10^{-9} metres.

Oil paintings: see page 137.

Oxidation: The combination of a substance with oxygen or a reaction in which the atoms of an element lose electrons and change their valency.

Paint cross-sections: Small paint samples taken from a painting under magnification, embedded in a resin block which is then ground down to reveal the layer structure of the paint and the pigments it contains.

Palaeobotany: The study of fossil plants.

Palaeontology: The study of ancient organisms and the environments in which they lived.

Paper – works of art: see page 58.

Paraloid B-72™: An ethyl methacrylate/methyl acrylate co-polymer, often used in conservation because of its stability and good ageing properties.

Pastiche: A work that is composed of parts taken from other items and connected together, often imitating another style.

Patina: The colour or fine coating of corrosion on the surface of a metal often acquired with age, though it can be intentionally applied. It is often used to describe the green coloured corrosion which covers ancient bronzes, coins and medals.

Pentiment: A change of composition made by the artist during painting, often visible in the finished work as a change in surface texture or dark shadow.

pH buffer: A substance that minimises change in the acidity of a solution when an acid or base is added to the solution.

Photon: A unit of electromagnetic energy which is uncharged and has no mass.

Photogrammetry: The process of obtaining reliable measurements or information from photographs or other sensing systems.

Plastazote™: A closed cell cross linked polyethylene foam that is blown using nitrogen. Tests show Plastazote™ foam is stable, safe and non-reactive when in contact with a variety of museum objects.

Plasticizers: Various substances added to plastics or other materials to make or keep them soft or pliable.

Polyethylene glycol: A water soluble wax, often used as a consolidant for waterlogged material and as a humectant or lubricant for leather.

Polymerase chain reaction (PCR): see page 23.

Portable Antiquities Scheme (PAS): see page 90.

Preservation: The prevention or delay of deterioration.

Propylene glycol: Viscous colourless aliphatic alcohol used in a variety of products such as food, cosmetics and anti-freeze.

Pseudomorphic: Term used to describe a mineral that has developed the form of another.

Puddling: A process developed in the late 18th century to purify iron by heating and working in the presence of oxygen, to free it from impurities and a portion of its carbon.

Pyrite decay: see page 159.

Quoin: One of a series of stones laid at the exterior corners and angles of a building.

Recitified photography: A cheaper but less accurate process than photogrammetry, where photos are taken of a facade to produce an accurate image. Only works properly when the facade is flat, and the camera is held exactly parallel to it.

Recto: The front of an object or the right hand page.

Red rot: An insidious form of the chemical degradation of leather caused by the use of inferior tannins and other chemicals during manufacture, and by exposure to atmospheric pollutants, especially sulphides. It is therefore common in leather bindings dating from the 19th century.

Refractive index: The refractive index (RI) of a substance is the ratio of the speed of light in a vacuum to the speed of light in the substance. It is a measure of the extent to which light is refracted when passing from one medium to another.

Relative humidity (RH): The ratio, expressed as a percentage, of the water vapour contained in the air compared to the maximum amount it could contain at that particular temperature and pressure.

Retouching: Layers of paint added by restorers or conservators to disguise damaged areas.

Scanning electron microscope (SEM): see page 92.

Semi-quantitative: Results that are more accurate than with a qualitative test, (which indicates constituents without proportions), but where the degree of precision is lower than those of a fully quantitive analysis.

Shale: see page 46.

Smalt: A deep blue vitreous pigment made from powdered glass coloured with cobalt.

SSSI: Site of Special Scientific Interest: an area that has been notified as being of special interest under the Wildlife and Countryside Act, 1981.

Stopping-out agent: A substance such as a varnish or other covering matter used to keep another substance from areas which are to be protected; it is often applied by brush.

Sublime: When a substance evaporates directly from its solid state to a vapour without forming a liquid.

Tabby weave: A simple weave structure also known as plain weave.

Taxonomy: The classification of organisms.

Treasure Act: see page 80.

UKIC: United Kingdom Institute of Conservation of Historic and Artistic Works. Became the Institute of Conservation (ICON) in 2005.

Underpainting: Initial layers of paint found directly on top of the ground layer, often brown or grey in colour, mapping out the basic elements of the composition.

Unguentarium: A small glass bottle or 'unguent flask' which probably contained medicines or perfumes.

Upset: To make the end of a metal bar or rivet shorter and thicker by hammering on the end.

Verso: The back of an object or the left hand page.

World Heritage Sites: Places or buildings of outstanding universal value and recognized as part of world heritage, designated by UNESCO. They include cultural, natural and mixed sites.

X-ray diffraction (XRD): see page 107.

X-radiography: see page 180.